RAF GROUND SUPPORT EQUIPMENT
SINCE 1918

RAF GROUND SUPPORT EQUIPMENT
SINCE 1918

F.J. Adkin

Airlife

Copyright © 1996 Fredk. J. Adkin

First published in the UK in 1996
by Airlife Publishing Ltd

British Library Cataloguing in Publication Data
A catalogue record for this book
is available from the British Library

ISBN 1 85310 562 7

Typeset by Phoenix Typesetting, Ilkley, West Yorkshire.
Printed in England by The Bath Press Ltd., Bath.

Airlife Publishing Ltd
101 Longden Road, Shrewsbury, SY3 9EB England.

CONTENTS

Foreword

As soon as the first aeroplane flew, it required technical tradesmen to keep it airworthy through maintenance, repair and modification. The men who were first available for these tasks were usually the aircraft's designer and his team, which probably comprised an engine mechanic, carpenter/joiner and fabric workers. But as the aeroplane caught on and was built in ever-increasing numbers, there was an increasing demand for the basic technical skills required. The introduction of the aircraft to the public in the form of air meetings and races before the First World War placed demands on the available aircraft tradesmen, who often had to work long hours to repair the machines that were easily bent – and often were.

In general the work was within the scope of the trained tradesmen, but they were few – the work was new and the internal combustion engine was still a rarity. As with all great technical innovations development was the natural outcome, but in those early years it was a leisurely process. Service aeroplanes were first developed by the Royal Aircraft Factory and later accepted by the Army, which called on the Royal Engineers to provide appropriate trades to service the aircraft. Operation of these was again a leisurely way of life in the last few years of peace as the service evaluated the technical development of engines and airframes of this new and advanced weapon. The demands of the First World War accelerated progress, which in turn called for special tools and equipment, most of which were sent to the great repair depots in France. In these depots much advanced thinking transformed them virtually into service factories, with powered machine shops and workshops for all eventualities. Rebuilds soon became normal practice.

Maintenance is an essential adjunct to the operation of aircraft – a truism of course. In the 'good old days', the ground equipment was as simple as the aircraft and as these developed over the years, so ground equipment remained static and the ground tradesmen who had to produce aircraft fit to fly often had to make do with out-of-date servicing equipment, relying on their own expertise and ingenuity to use ground equipment, however primitive or makeshift it might be. The technical development of such equipment applicable to aircraft servicing and maintenance has proceeded on roughly parallel lines to aircraft progress, the period enveloping the biplane era generally remaining as static as the aeroplanes themselves. In some cases design has enabled equipment to become 'universal', such as trestles, to meet smoothly some of the requirements of the metal monoplane era.

Such was the stringent economy imposed on the services in the years between the wars that much of the early ground equipment, suitably modified as required, was in use in the RAF from 1920 to 1939 and even later. This was only possible because the type of equipment required in the biplane era was almost universal. Only with the threat of war bringing in the modern monoplane was ground equipment to become more complex and of greater variety. The coming of the latter aircraft began not only a revolution in aircraft design, but also in their associated ground equipment; since then both aircraft and equipment have developed on parallel, complementary paths.

With the coming of the propulsion reaction (jet) aircraft, together with the breakthrough in electronic science, aircraft have rapidly become larger, faster, higher flying and much more complex. To cope with this the required – and often very specialised – equipment has become equally sophisticated and more numerous in type. Whereas previously the normal flying unit ground crew trades could manage most aspects of operating and routine servicing of their own associated equipment

– with specialist help from station workshops – it became obvious that the increasing amount of equipment was requiring too much extra work for the aircraft trades. A new trade was finally introduced specifically for their maintenance, repair and operation. Aircraft ground equipment had come of age and now has its own major servicing and storage units within the envelope of Maintenance Command.

Perhaps the most well known of these was one of the oldest in service, No. 16 MU at RAF Stafford, which maintains and stores a vast amount of the RAF's ground equipment. This particular MU has justifiably made a name for itself by the excellence of its products. All the machines illustrated in this account will have been serviced, repaired, renovated, restored, processed and, if necessary reduced to produce by this unit.

Ground service equipment, as it was first known – it was later to be ground support equipment (GSE) – encompassed not only RAF aircraft use, but also a very wide range of other, non-aircraft items. Because of the great range any attempt to describe these could be boring and turn this account into a catalogue. So, a representative number of GSE units have been chosen to give some indication of the range from simple to sophisticated of the units utilised in keeping aircraft and accessories serviceable, the thought that has gone into their design and production and, in use, the high-quality maintenance required.

GSE is not usually mentioned in books dealing with aviation. One of the main reasons for this is that the technicalities of equipment and machines do not make very interesting reading for the majority as against, say, an epic flight or wartime operation or a glamorous aeroplane. But if the aircraft is to give its designed performance, to bring success to an operation or help the hotshot pilot, it is dependent on efficient maintenance. The depth of detail of equipment and machine presented to the reader is a difficult test for the author, for at what level does he write? In this book I have endeavoured to find the happy mean, hopefully giving sufficient detail to satisfy the technical reader without overwhelming the non-technical one.

Acknowledgements

I wish to express my sincere thanks for help unstintingly given by the Station Commanders of RAF stations Brize Norton, Cosford, Cottesmore, St Athan, Stafford and Valley for permission to visit, and to the following Engineer Officers: Wing Commander P.G.E. Murray, Squadron Leaders R.B. Mills and G. Roberts, Flight Lieutenants A. Barratt, V.W. Carter, K.G. Kline, A. Whiting and Warrant Officers C. Godney and D. Lovatt. Also to Flight Sergeants J.C. Bole and Howarth, Chief Technician Gough and Sergeants M. Gunn and E. Owen.

My thanks also to Mr L. Woodgate, ex F/Lt Engineer and retired Keeper of the Aerospace Museum, Cosford, and to the following civilian firms who gave their help wherever it was possible: Julie Cox, Sales Department, Access Equipment Ltd; Mr T. Dodd, Office Manager, Aircraft Maintenance Supply Services; Lois Spencer, Group PR, Auto Diesel Braby Ltd; Mr F.B. Still, Main Tractor Division, Ford of Europe; Mr M. Moulton, Information Executive, GEC Avionics; Mr T. Mathias, Sales Manager, Grove Coles Ltd; Mr R.B. Buss, Contracts Manager, Houchin Ltd; Mr J. Lawrie, FRSC, Chief Chemist, Kilfrost Ltd; Mr D. Hoyland, Market Department, Martin Baker Aircraft Co. Ltd; Mr G. Smith, Mr R.R. Green, Technical Market Executive, ML Aviation Co. Ltd; Mr G. Grace, Information Officer, Murex Welding Products Ltd; Mr D.G. Crudginton, Sales Division, Power Lifts Ltd; Mr A. Knight, RFD Aviation Ltd; Mr S.P.W. Lines, Marketing Manager, Simon-Gala Ltd; Mr A.J. Combe, Managing Director, Sturtevant Engineering Co Ltd.

Photo Credits

Organisations:
AMSS; David Brown Ltd; Coles International; Flight International; Ford of Europe; HML; Houchin; IWM; ML Aviation Co Ltd; Ministry of Defence; Murex; Normalair-Garret; RAF Museum; RAF Stafford; Royal Aeronautical Society; Simon Engineering; Sturtevant Engineering Co Ltd.

Individuals:
J.M. Bruce; C.C.H. Coles; A. Eaton; S.A.C. Francis; R. Honeybone; J. Hughes; H. Kevin; S. Leslie; F. Marchant; K. Marshall; R. Milner; J.P. Murray; F/S Nicholl; Sgt Noble; R. Phillips; C/T Powell; Bruce Robertson; F/Lt Rushton; RFD; D. Tattershall; R. Lee.

My sincere thanks to all the contributors and to Mr Chris Brown who processed the remainder of the black and white prints, by the author.

Finally, my sincere acknowledgements to Mr Peter Coles of Airlife who, by subtle and judicious editing, has made the text flow more easily and accurately.

Chapter 1

What is GSE?

First, to answer the question set out in the title, the original definition of ground support equipment was any item of RAF equipment which materially helps in the servicing and maintenance of aircraft, motor transport, marine craft and some aspects of general maintenance, either by improving efficiency or by reducing the time the job takes, or both. We shall look at the modern definition later in this chapter.

Secondly, look on the apron or flight line of almost any civilian or RAF operational station and you may see a variety of two- or four-wheeled units clustered around an aircraft, most connected to it by electric cable or hose and to which the aircraft appears technically subordinate. These are the latest versions in the array of GSE, designed to make the complex servicing of modern aircraft substantially easier for the ground tradesmen. And these are but a few of the many facilities available.

GSE in 1918 was minimal. There was little need of any comprehensive range of servicing for the simple aeroplanes of the day, and the new RAF, born of war, was operating under conditions of war in which any surplus GSE was just a dream – the norm was to operate with the absolute minimum. On a normal front-line squadron, this comprised such items as stepladders, trestles, chocks, refuelling bowsers, air pumps, racks and engine stands, sheer legs, hoists and pickets. Secondary equipment comprised mainly brushes, fabric sewing machines, carpenters' benches, flat-top trailers for salvaging; some lucky units might have one of the mobile workshop lorries, open and fitted with a lathe, forge, drilling machine and grinder. Those that did not had to acquire them if they could, or go without. Combined with the issue toolkits, that was about it.

When the RAF began to reorganise its technical content after the First World War all ground equipment with mechanical components, such as sheer legs and gantries, air pumps, petrol and oil bowsers, all salvage equipment, rigging instruments, MT tools and equipment and even items of barrack equipment were lumped under the general title of ground servicing equipment. The storage of this equipment was rather loosely organised. Generally, most mechanically operated and/or engine-driven units were stored in, or under the control of, station workshops. The remainder of items specific to resident squadrons were usually stored in that unit's hangar and ancillary workshops. Hangar-stored GSE was usually grouped according to the whim and tidiness of the squadron Engineer Officer (EO), Warrant Officer (WO) or Flight Sergeant (F/Sgt) in charge, and this was reflected also in the quality of presentation and mechanical condition.

In the years between the world wars the work of the RAF tradesmen was entirely within their own skills. If an engine, aircraft or ancillary equipment went unserviceable, the relevant tradesman saw the whole job through from start to finish, including testing, just as they do today. But they did the job with a toolbox containing a well-worn kit of tools, the loss of any of which they would have to pay for, specialist manufacturing tools such as special spanners, propeller and engine toolkits, rigging instruments and with the minimum of GSE, mainly because there was so little.

The years between the wars were notorious for the penny-pinching policy imposed by successive governments which restricted progress, and (only) from the point of view of aircraft and equipment relegated the RAF to a lower scale in the world's air forces. The RAF's reaction to this was to become the most efficient air force by virtue of better maintenance of its aircraft and equally better training of its ground and air staff. Superiority of actual aircraft and equipment came when the Expansion Scheme of 1934 opened the floodgates to modern sophisticated

Three views of the general engineering section of a typical station workshop, that of RAF Finningley in February 1984. From top:

Servicing bay for Viper prop jet engine and propellers of a Jetstream aircraft, with a mobile tool rack at right.

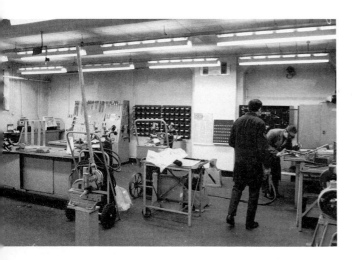

The machine shop, showing well-maintained but rather elderly lathes, grinder, etc.

aircraft – which required equally modern ground equipment for their servicing.

The servicing of ground equipment had been rather a slap-happy affair prior to the Expansion period and before the creation of a trade group for this work. On a busy pre-war flight first things were first and ground equipment servicing waited its turn, although it is fair to say that whenever there were slack days due to bad weather ground equipment was given a degree of priority. Mechanics were detailed as and when convenient, or the work was strictly necessary, and a form of servicing record was kept, usually comprising the dates of the previous servicing, when the next was due and, towards the end of this period, the class of equipment. But when the servicing was done it was thoroughly done. In the years 1918–33 service aircraft showed very little progress in basic design, 'new' models being mainly developed versions of the biplane. As a result, GSE requirements were a matter of job commitment, with more emphasis on ordinary tools. Stepladders, gantries, sheer legs, chocks, refuelling bowsers, gun-synchronising gear and bomb transporters remained much as before in design, although such items as trestles, engine stands and refuellers made some progress; tail trolleys were introduced, together with tower ladders, for example. Just as the evolution of the biplane was the result of dominant thought tempered by economics, so was the equipment that supported their servicing.

A major revision of ground equipment was undertaken in 1929–31 to standardise as much of the existing GSE as possible. This saw the scrapping of much that was obsolescent. Attempts were made to make some equipment 'universal', difficult when new aircraft were introduced. All GSE was reviewed and new equipment was brought in, subject to its effectiveness under hard-service use. At this time, as a constant reminder to the user units to make an item last as long as possible, the Air Publication 1086 included a priced vocabulary of all Air Ministry stores.

The arrival of the monoplane aircraft on to stations geared to operating biplanes required much new ground equipment. Station workshops were re-equipped with better machines, tools and facilities more suited to their new tasks. From 1934, with the advent of the all-metal monoplanes (Anson excepted), there was a dramatic increase in numbers and types of GSE, leading to more specialist ground equipment; the larger size of some aircraft also called for better access facilities. Hydraulic jacking super-seded mechanical trestling on most aircraft, better hoists were introduced for the heavier engine and air-craft components such as propellers, larger-capacity fuel tanks led to the need for greater capacity and faster refuelling bowsers, the use of high-pressure air

for aircraft systems and paint spraying saw power-driven air compressors begin to enter service. Moving of aircraft was revised and modernised. Larger bomb loads and greater amounts of gun ammunition carried for the multi-gunned fighters and turreted bombers revised the design of arma-ment GSE. In the ancillary workshops of electrical, instrument, radio/radar the new systems fitted to the aircraft required specialist skills and the GSE to utilise these skills. It was all beginning to happen.

Aeroplanes, being the precision machines they are and exceedingly vulnerable to rapid demise in the event of mechanical failure – or pilot error – are given regular and thorough inspections to minimise the likelihood of faults occurring and to maintain their undoubted pre-eminence in reliability. The inspection cycles are based on hours flown, or oper-ated, with some specialist systems subject to a different cycle, such as tyres which are on a 'number of landings' basis. The complexity of the inspections

Ground support equipment parked on a misty day at the rear of the Engineering Flight of RAF Finningley in February 1984, showing starters, heater trolley and other GSE.

GSE servicing bay at RAF Cottesmore station workshops, with electrical starter trolleys undergoing servicing. Note the ideal floor surface. July 1987.

is in direct proportion to the type of aircraft, the early biplanes being straightforward in their requirements with a minimum of moving parts or systems on the airframe, the engine being the major mechanical item; radio and electrical power was also at a minimum.

To service and maintain the crop of GSE before and during the Second World War, a more efficient form of servicing with accurate records was devised, the items graded in order of mechanical efficiency and degree of service requirements. The GSE was categorised into three main classes for the purpose of servicing cycles, with schedules made up accordingly. The classes were:

Class 1   All equipment which utilises a form of power for its operation, i.e. petrol, diesel, electrical and, when the jet entered service, the jet turbine. Servicing schedules were issued and signed for on servicing record forms and inspections carried out daily, weekly and monthly.

Class 2   All equipment with moving parts, i.e. hydraulic jacks, hoists, etc. No servicing schedules issued at first but were issued later; inspections were carried out weekly and monthly, and signed for on servicing record forms.

Class 3   Fixed equipment such as chocks, ladders, drip trays, etc. No servicing schedules; inspections carried out monthly and quarterly, and signed for.

In general, the servicing system of aircraft, ground equipment, MT, marine craft and so on was carried out from 1940 by a specialist servicing squadron on the station in order of depth of technical servicing.

With the introduction of Planned Flying and Planned Servicing in 1948 there was a revision of the system which, although staying basically in its original scheme, was broken down into four main 'lines'; in each line was placed the requisite skills of manpower, equipment, spares and so on. The original scheme was revised to ensure that all aspects of servicing would comply with the new scheme. The lines are:

First line servicing. Day-to-day routine servicing, minor defects and rectification, carrying out any special instruction, replacement of items of equipment.

Second line servicing. Superseded the servicing squadrons introduced at the beginning of WW2 and included minor and major servicing. Rectification of defects beyond the capacity of first line.

Third line servicing. Usually sited in maintenance depots to do more specialised work beyond the capacity of first and second line. Its equivalent in the 1920s and 1930s would be station workshops.

Fourth line servicing. Normally all major work which generally required the assistance of manufacturers.

Post-WW1 the servicing of GSE was originally carried out on a split basis, the heavier mechanical items by station workshops and the 'fixed' items (chocks, trestles, etc.) by the user unit. This state of affairs carried on quite happily until after the outbreak of WW2, when the great increase in GSE and manpower enabled user units to carry out most

General view of the engineering bays of 4 Flight at 16 MU RAF Stafford, showing the comprehensive servicing equipment available for major overhauls. 6 July 1993 *(RAF Official ST/440.93)*.

of the servicing of its own GSE, with the possible exception of power-driven units, which were still done by station workshops, servicing squadrons and/or MT.

The great increase in importance of GSE after WW2, plus its growing versatility and complexity, created a problem in that servicing squadrons and user units were either loth to divert scarce specialist aircraft trades (man and woman power had declined dramatically) to service these units to the high standards now mandatory, or they still foisted the work on to the overloaded general engineering trades under station workshops, who were really more trained for this work; when the new Trade Structure was introduced in 1951 the latter were made the nucleus of the new ground equipment trades, but it was the advent of the specialised servicing trolleys plus all the normal equipment that finally brought the problem to a head. The decision was then made

to introduce new specialist trades from the cadre of the workshop engineering trades plus any other suitable tradesmen who wished to remuster. The trades are:

General Technician Ground Support Equipment (Gen Tech GSE)
General Mechanic Ground Support Equipment (Gen Mech GSE)

The basic unit on a station – superseding the old station workshop – is the General Engineering Flight (GEF), which includes the new trades and is directly under the control of the station Engineer Officer.

To back up this trade structure there has developed a full separate organisation and administration formation similar to any in Support Command, with its own maintenance units and storage units, controlling many millions of pounds' worth of expensive ground support equipment.

Post-WW2, the politics of the Cold War decided the pattern on which the RAF was to base its forward-planning tactics and strategy. Among the

General view of 4 Flight at 16 MU RAF Stafford on 6 July 1993, showing electrical trolleys under servicing and fully equipped to carry out all major servicing requirements *(RAF Official ST/441.93)*.

The crest of 4 Flight, no. 2 Engineering Squadron, based on 16 MU RAF Stafford, the staff of which were representative of all the squadrons, flights and stations visited in the course of research for this book – most helpful.

created one of the great changes brought about by their introduction, the formation of the new trades needed to maintain this mass of machinery. Such was the increase in GSE and tradesmen that a maintenance unit, RAF Stafford, is now devoted almost entirely to their storage, issue and deep servicing.

Today's ground servicing equipment is now defined as 'items of mechanical and electrical equipment which are used in the maintenance or operational support of aircraft and associated systems, weapon systems, airfield facilities, marine craft (now defunct), MT, synthetic trainers and ground radio installations' and is broken down as follows:

Standard GSE.	Equipment which is applicable to more than one aircraft or system type.
Special to type.	Equipment which is applicable to a specific aircraft or system type.
Aerospace ground equipment (AGE).	Certain items of GSE used on Tornado aircraft

direct tactical concepts was that of the fast turn round of operational aircraft, admirably exemplified by the fighter aircraft, which was sufficient for all practical purposes in the immediate post-war years. However, the new deadly menace with the pointed nose could not be intercepted and made a slight mockery of fighter-type scrambles, although these were retained for operating against the intrusion of high-flying recce aircraft, usually Russian. The nuclear bomb altered current tactics completely and when the 'retaliatory concept' came into use for the V bombers, the vital importance of fast standby take offs and the use of GSE to speed that operation came to assume a war-winning, or losing, significance.

The great idea of achieving fast turn rounds, using the new starter GSE, for example, was somewhat spoiled in the beginning by the units themselves being bulky and requiring a definite drill for starting, in addition to MT drivers for the towing vehicles. The variety of power units within the GSE for their operation needed, in turn, a knowledge which added further technology to the relatively simple task of starting an aero engine. This increased complexity and extra knowledge expanded steadily to cope with the new designs and

Not to scale

Refueller

Hydraulic servicing rig

Refueller

Air starter

Baggage truck

Aircraft toilet servicing

H P air servicing

Oxygen

Cabin heating/cooling

Diagrammatic layout of ground support equipment that could be required on a service aircraft on turn-round. It also illustrates flight-line clutter.

environment, but which comply with RAF GSE maintenance procedures, except where multi-national procedures are specified.

The Planned Servicing lines of maintenance have now been given a different definition:

First Line — Maintenance organisation under the responsibility of CO of · user unit for carrying out replenishment, adjusting specified preventative maintenance, initial defect diagnosis and limited corrective maintenance. For major GSE General Engineering Flight would carry out depth A and B maintenance as required and for minor GSE first-line maintenance is the user unit.

Second Line — Maintenance organisation under the CO of user unit established for the control and maintenance of user's GSE but excluding first-line organisation.

Third Line — GSE maintenance organisa-

A Tornado GR Mk 1 (T) aircraft surrounded by some of the ground support equipment needed to maintain it in service. Taken at the Tri-National Tornado Training Establishment at RAF Cottesmore (SAC Francis, RAF Official).

Fourth Line

tion within the services, but excluding organisation within first and second line. Independent maintenance organisation providing repair, modifications and reconditioning under contract (usually a MU).

In line with the high engineering standards demanded of modern GSE, the GSE is painted in colours and treatment which have a definite purpose, for which three reasons are given:

1 Operational. Camouflage within operational environment.
2 Anti-deterioration. As the title describes.
3 Appearance. Maintaining a high military appearance which also determines extent and frequency of repainting

The colours are:

Infra-red reflecting green for operational role deployed outside base.
Dark green gloss standard finish for all other GSE.
Safety devices in red matt.
Unit markings stencilled white on canopy and chassis.
Maintenance operating instructions stencilled black where appropriate.
Recognition colour discs.
Anti-collision yellow strip adhesive markings fixed longitudinally.

The units described in the following chapters have been chosen as representative ground support equipment in service over the long period from 1918 to a depth of technical detail that it is hoped most readers will understand.

Chapter 2

Ground Movement

Without power to provide mobility an aircraft is, as I have written elsewhere, just a piece of shapely, expensive, useless junk. The engine(s) were normally used in the early years to taxi or move the aircraft when sufficient manpower was not available until, as aircraft increased in size and weight, it was found that:

1. It was more convenient, and became the norm, to manhandle an aircraft in confined spaces.
2. As engines developed it was found that excessive taxiing was detrimental to the servicing cycle life and gave problems of overheating.
3. When jet engines came into general service it was both unsafe to airfield personnel and uneconomical in fuel usage just to move the aircraft under the power of these engines.

So, as prior to 1939 aircraft were normally kept in hangars, 'before you flew 'em you pushed 'em'. In the very early years of lightweight, fragile machines, this presented no problems – the mechanic simply hoisted the tail on to his shoulder and walked; the early nose undercarriage pusher types could be moved easily by two men. In 1910, a tentative attempt had been made to tow using a motor car to offset the then minimal manpower of the Royal Engineers Air Corps, but the structural weakness on the ground of the early types, further magnified by the rough field conditions precluded this as a standard method.

Later, during the Great War, the ground move-

Possibly the first photo of an aircraft being towed in the manner which was to remain unchanged until towing reached the stage of fixed towbars and nose-wheel application. Quite a team was required to assist the car and keep an eye open for possible snags. The date is 1913 and the car is MOD.

BREGUET BIPLANE WITH ENGINE TROUBLE BEING TOWED BACK TO HANGAR. FARNBORO.
F. SCOVELL. 31.

A Handley Page 0/100 being towed by a Clayton tractor, powered by a 35–40hp Dorman Stafford engine. Note that the towing ropes were simply tied to a suitable strong point on the undercarriage, rather than to definite attachment points. The tractor was made by Clayton and Shuttleworth *(Bruce Robertson Collection)*.

ment of heavy multi-engined aircraft began to present further problems on muddy Flanders fields, despite the then plentiful manpower available. Handley Page carried out successful towing trials with their 0/100 bombers, using an early Clayton caterpillar tractor – even a horse had been used – but towing by tractor was not universally adopted, and was used even less after WW1. Throughout this conflict the vast majority of land aircraft were moved by manpower and as size and weight increased the problem of manoeuvring them by steering increased. Consequently, in about 1917, the tail trolley made its first appearance. This item was probably among the first really useful pieces of ground equipment.

To steer more easily in and out of the hangar several types of tailskid trolley were evolved, the type depending on the use and weight of the aircraft. An early model consisted of a single tapered metal arm

to which at the trolley end was fitted a raised bracket to contain the skid and two small cast-iron wheels. Another was rather quaint in appearance, comprising a single tubular axle, at each end of which was fitted a small caterpillar track. In the axle centre was a double bracket to which was fitted an extension to fit under the bottom of the fin, or rear fuselage sternpost, and from the bracket extended a single tubular arm with tee handle for the operator. That unit was not placed into service!

Most generally used of these items was merely a wooden box, open at the top, which was mounted on the centre of a fixed axle, at each end of which was an iron-tyred wheel. Secured at each end of the axle – or in the centre – was an arm to a common handle. The tail of the aircraft was lifted and the tailskid dropped into the box; the aircraft could now be pushed and easily steered. The 'laying on of hands' by enthusiastic, burly mechanics had brought a few inevitable problems, such as damaged nose riblets, until it was inculcated in them that the strong points for pushing were not necessarily the same in the aerodynamic sense. With slight modifications to trolleys this method of ground movement became the basic method until tailskids gave way to tail wheels.

That war over and RAF peacetime routine estab-

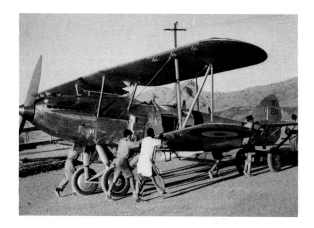

A Hawker Hart of 11 or 39 Squadron at RAF Peshawar in 1936, being given the 'laying on of hands' into the hangar. Note the early box-type tail steering trolley. This aircraft crashed north-east of Ambala on 3 August 1943 (J.P. Murray).

A steering arm fitted to a Tempest at RAF St Athan in September 1986, showing the cable release for disconnecting the steering-arm lugs from the tail-wheel fork. Just above the tailwheel, in the lower fuselage, can be seen the hole to take a lifting beam for trestling.

lished, with a drastic reduction of the ample manpower of the war, the traditional leaning-on style of moving aircraft was carried on and the hangars began to resound to shouts of 'Two Six' every working day, morning and afternoon, to get together the necessary numbers of men to push the aircraft out to be lined up or inside the hangars to their respective bays. With the large aircraft every effort was made to use engine power to taxi as much as possible. Before WW2 it was known that sometimes, particularly at night, when manpower was minimal, unauthorised use of engine power was made to taxi aircraft right inside the hangar. But inevitably it took men to place the aircraft in their final position. Reliable, suitable tractors were still in the future and the eventual use of these was boosted by the civil airlines.

On these airlines the need was to have large aircraft capable of carrying more passengers and when this was practically realised, with the introduction into service of such types as the Handley Page W8 and Armstrong Whitworth Argosy, the sight to passengers of large numbers of men pushing an airliner was not considered a good advert for a progressive airline. But the airlines had even less manpower than the services, so some tentative towing experiments were once again carried out, an early half-track caterpillar being successfully used by one airline.

This fluctuating state of affairs continued until the arrival of the really heavy aircraft of the early

1930s – the Fairey Hendon, Handley Page Harrow and Heyford, Bristol Bombay are examples – followed by the Expansion breed of all-metal monoplanes meant that a method of moving aircraft less dependent on manpower (although this would never be) was needed. Like so much progress that was made at this time the advent of tail-wheeled aircraft and air-operated brakes, and the introduction into the RAF of the Fordson 'agricultural' tractor were the catalysts to ground-movement progression. Aircraft were still pushed, but now without the steering trolley: manufacturers had introduced the steering arm. This useful item was usually in the form of a welded tubular steel assembly, shaped to

A towing arm of the early type, fitted to a Valetta at the Aerospace Museum in Cosford, September 1986.

A standard tail steering arm minus its fork locking pins and cable, at the Aerospace Museum in Cosford, February 1988.

accommodate a cross handle at one end and two fork ends at the other to fit over, or into, lugs on the tail-wheel forks. It made the pushing and manoeuvring much easier. Later developments of the steering arm veered towards universal models, with tail-wheel forks having either bobbins or slots for the steering-arm forks which in turn had cable-operated pins to secure the arm. There were long and short versions with some types adjustable for width.

The first successful Fordson was developed from the agricultural model with very little modification, changing the original spiked wheels for the well-known 'track grip' tyres being the largest 'mod'. It had early been considered as a prime mover for towing and in its modified form had been, and was, used for the movement of fuel bowsers. Despite its early fault of not being able to change gear on the move, with consequent lack of acceleration, it was used to tow aircraft, initially by rope cables from the front. The gear-changing fault was later rectified. With practice, and not a few mistakes, a technique was evolved and a drill laid down. Towing was virtually confined to multi-engined aircraft as the single-engine types were more easily managed by pushing.

The towing of an aeroplane in those days proceeded thus:

The NCO or senior airman i/c the team checked the ground equipment required, ensured that the aircraft had sufficient brake air pressure and detailed his team as follows: one airman in the cabin/cockpit on the brakes, one at each wing-tip, a responsible airman on the steering arm and placed himself where he could be seen and see all.

The tractor, usually driven by an MT driver, had been connected to the front of the aircraft by a rope bridle (wire cables were subsequently used) from the towing eye of the tractor to a strong point on each undercarriage leg, usually the top of the oleo leg area. When all was ready the i/c gave the order, the driver tried to accelerate smoothly – not always easy on a Fordson – and the entourage moved off.

On a straight line course the onus was on both tractor driver and steerer to maintain it; it was on the curves that teamwork was so important. And it was here that early towing faults showed up. Problems could arise when turning if the arc of the turn was not maintained through the centre line of the tractor, the aeroplane and steerer, or if the emphasis of correct control was not with the steerer. If he increased or decreased the arc it had the effect of driving the aircraft to right or left of the tractor, with the risk of collision with the tractor; another risk was that the ropes would be made unequal in apparent length by one slackening, which had the effect of allowing one undercarriage wheel to overrun the slack rope.

The NCO i/c the team had to watch for these

The Fordson agricultural tractor of the late 1920s. From this, through the addition of heavy-duty tyres and other modifications, was developed the RAF towing tractor which did such a good job during its long service (Ford of Europe).

David Brown Taskmaster 1948–65 tractor used for towing aircraft, shown here at a tractor rally. Developed from the Cropmaster, it had a four-speed gearbox which was later superseded by a six-speed unit. Later models had a fluid-drive torque converter (D. Tattershall).

points and correct either the steerer, the tractor driver, or both; if an emergency was developing, he would call out 'Brakes' (loudly) to the man in the cabin making sure that the driver could also stop, to avoid the rope being broken or a dangerous strain being thrown on the rope-attachment point. It can be seen that the man on the brakes had a responsible job in his application of them.

The author was a victim of one such occurrence when towing a Hudson from a hangar which had a distinct slope on to the tarmac, on a very early and dark morning. The aircraft gained speed, the tractor was unable to accelerate sufficiently, the steerer tried to turn the aircraft to avoid overrunning the tractor and the man in the cabin, despite frantic shouts of 'Brakes!' slept peacefully on. Result, the starboard prop struck tractor and author, fortunately at slow enough speed to hurt prop and author only slightly, although the tractor was badly damaged.

This always makeshift method was used just prior to WW2 and into it, until accidents and the introduction of the largest aircraft of the war – Stirling, Lancaster, Halifax and York – demanded more safety and control in ground movement; as a result the steering arm and forward towing were substituted by the towbar and backward towing from the aircraft tail-wheel. Immediately, new teething problems arose, caused by the rigidity of the towbar, which initially had no shock-absorbing qualities (although these were built into later models) and lacked the 'give' of rope or cable. The tail-wheel structure, not designed for this stress, simply could not stand the harsh forces imposed by rigid towbars (and inexperienced drivers) and the sudden pull on take off from heavy tractors, or harsh braking. In these early days tail-wheel forks were frequently wrenched off.

Confining towing to smooth, flat surfaces only was a temporary answer and a longer-term solution was soon found in two main modifications. First, the tail-wheel assemblies were strengthened on the production line, and secondly, more vital and quicker, a spring-loaded fail-safe device was fitted into the towbars. When the pulling load of the tractor almost reached the designed strength of the tail-wheel assembly, such as when it was pulling the aircraft uphill or over uneven ground, the preset spring-loading in the towbar operated to disengage locking pins in the fork of the towbar from the tail-wheel fork. Subsequent modifications made the release mechanism adjustable to suit types of aircraft. This was fitted into the draw-bar and automatically released if an overload occurred. The towbars were also made to 'break' in the bar itself, rather than at the tail-wheel fork.

The use of a tractor greatly reduced, for example, the time required to check swing an aircraft's

A heavy-duty, general-purpose tail towing arm at RAF Cosford servicing squadron, after being reconditioned and equipped with a Canberra nose-wheel fitting. This arm is also fitted with an adjustable, spring-loaded release. September 1986.

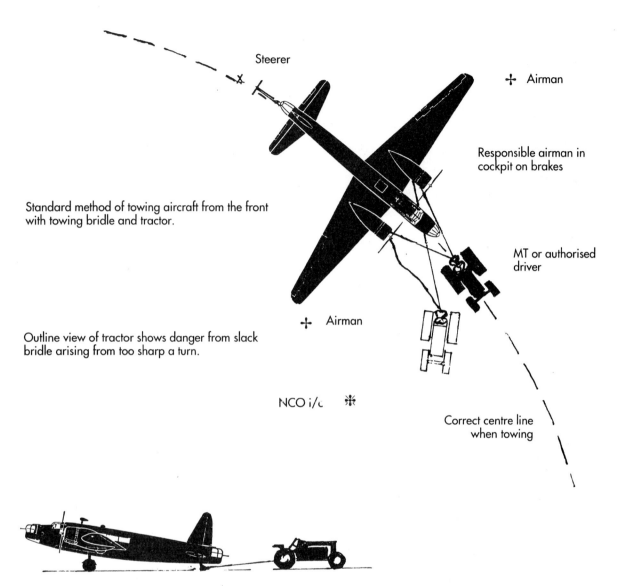

Steerer

+ Airman

Standard method of towing aircraft from the front with towing bridle and tractor.

Responsible airman in cockpit on brakes

MT or authorised driver

+ Airman

Outline view of tractor shows danger from slack bridle arising from too sharp a turn.

NCO i/c ❋

Correct centre line when towing

Normal towing from tail-wheel with towbar and tractor.

Normal towing from nose-wheel with towbar and tractor.

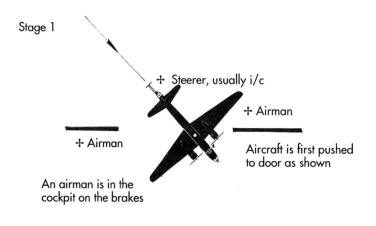

Stage 1

+ Steerer, usually i/c

+ Airman

+ Airman

Aircraft is first pushed
to door as shown

An airman is in the
cockpit on the brakes

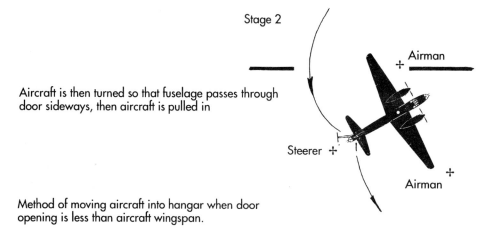

Stage 2

Airman
+

Aircraft is then turned so that fuselage passes through
door sideways, then aircraft is pulled in

Steerer +

+
Airman

Method of moving aircraft into hangar when door
opening is less than aircraft wingspan.

compass with much less manpower and obviated the need to be confined to the single previously specifically installed concrete base compass point. And moving a whole flight's aircraft was much expedited.

One of the best examples of logical thinking in the field of towing was the combined steering/towing assembly unit, for naval use only, which consisted of a base fork unit adjustable to give a range of widths between jaws from 5⅛in (13cm) to 11in (28cm) and a long and short towing and/or steering arm, any of which could be fitted to the fork unit. The assembly could handle aircraft up to a weight of 20,000lb (9072kg). Soon a great variety of towbars were in service and in the search for a 'universal' type some were made to be lengthened by the provision of an extension piece which could be added between the towbar frame and the adaptor fork to increase the length by 4ft (1.2m).

The introduction of nose-wheel aircraft undercarriage made the whole procedure of towing much safer, with more direct control by the tractor driver; the present types of towbar are directly attached to built-in points on the nose-wheel. The very large and heavy aircraft such as the V bombers and transports, the VC10 for example, had specific towbars and required the use of specially designed tractor units of greater weight and traction, but still utilised the same method of towing. The strength of the nose-wheel assembly was increased to allow these tractors to push the aircraft rearwards for better control by the tractor driver. Most small aircraft, including fighters, have towing points (the Hawk for example) and some have their specialist towbar.

It was in the overcrowded hangars of the few years before the war, and the first winter of that war, that great skill in aircraft movement was an asset. The flow of the tide of new aircraft pouring into the

A Gnat Trainer being towed by a David Brown tractor at, possibly, Central Flying School, Little Rissington. Date not known *(Bruce Robertson Collection)*.

RAF had washed against inadequate hangar capacity with a risk of flooding, a state of affairs that had apparently not been foreseen and that was further compounded by the RAF's aversion to leaving aeroplanes out in the open in peacetime. So at the beginning and end of every day's work 'hangar draughts' were performed in getting too

The massive towbar required for moving a Vulcan, showing the points of attachment and the towbar mobility wheels. The safety spring-loaded release is in the main bar. Aerospace Museum, Cosford, June 1985.

many aircraft out of and into the hangar. Here the skilful were in demand. Two of the worst types of aircraft to manipulate were the Wellesley and Wellington, with wingspans quite out of proportion to their length (high aspect ratio and very efficient aerodynamically). A method of getting the disproportionate span into the hangar is shown (see page 26).

After WW2 the same conditions of reduced manpower and enforced economies as had appertained after WW1 meant that other suitable MT was used. The Land-rover, for example, proved to be a useful towing vehicle for some of the lighter aircraft, and flight personnel were able to qualify for driving licences to do this, thus saving the use of an MT driver. The picture of a Land-rover towing a Vampire (see page 30) illustrates this. Vehicles subsequently developed for specialised towing passed under Motor Transport control.

One unique method of moving aircraft was first carried out in the 1920s. Described as Skate, Sideways Tracking, it enabled the craft to be moved sideways. The Skate comprised a rectangular platform with raised edges and a castoring wheel at each corner. That used for the main wheel was provided with hinged chocks at each end which could be swung over to act as ramps up which the aircraft was pushed. A small skate was used under the tail and all further movement was by manpower. From this piece of equipment was developed the Side Tracking Skate type of 1952, used as a specialist item for the Blackburn Beverley transport of 1955, surely one of

An Edgehill 10ft (3m) towing bar used at RAF Brize Norton for towing TriStar aircraft. July 1987.

A towing arm (aircraft unknown) at the Aerospace Museum, Cosford, 8 July 1992.

the tallest aeroplanes ever built and much too high at the fin when on its skate for the fin to clear the lintel of a standard RAF hangar. The type E Skate was made as a dual item, two skates being coupled together by an adjustable link bar and fitted with two small wheels that ran on metal rails. Much precision was required in manoeuvring the aircraft up the 6 x 4ft (1.8 x 1.2m) ramps on to the skates. The type E was quickly superseded by a more flexible type F, with improved wheel jacking; it deleted the rails and was much more suitable for the Beverley. This type comprised a low platform with a ground clearance of only ½in (13mm), on four wheels with a metal-covered wood ramp of 6 x 4ft (1.8 x 1.2m) placed at right angles to the platform, up which the main wheels of the Beverley were towed. The skate for the nose-wheel incorporated an adjustable jack so that when in position the nose-wheel could be raised to lower the tail unit to give the necessary clearance under the door lintel and roof trusses. The aircraft was moved sideways into the hangar by towing, to a bay where the fin and rudder would project up between the roof trusses when the aircraft was levelled. All skates were then securely chocked.

From the early 1950s new flight line, or tarmac, ground equipment was being introduced in the form of heavy ground power units (GPUs), which required a tractor to move them. On a busy station with aircraft constantly coming and going this entailed a driver always standing by the tractor. This inconvenient state of affairs was accepted until a definite breakthrough in ground handling was made

with the use of an Aircraft Handler. Designed primarily for the crowded decks of the Royal Navy's carriers by ML Aviation, it was an instant success, requiring one man only to operate it and capable of moving aircraft and mobile weights of up to 20,000lb (9072kg) and helicopters. Its use was also instantly recognised by the RAF, but its introduction in the 1960s on to RAF stations was somewhat tardy. It was a dream item and dispensed with most of the normal towing paraphernalia.

The lack of recognition of this item seems even more belated if one considers that a handler based on this principle was available in 1931, when two prototypes of a 'powered tail trolley' were considered for service. The trolleys, which differed only in their towing capacity, had caterpillar wheels and the power unit at the driven end, where there was also a lifting arm. At the opposite end of the channel section tapered vee chassis were a castoring wheel, the lifting and traction controls and the steering handle. This promising piece of equipment, which would have preceded the ML mechanical handler by over twenty years, was, unfortunately, not taken up.

About 1955, Lansing Bagnall introduced one of the first aircraft-handler type tractor units. This handler was electrically powered and controlled by the one operator from the steering arm. The aircraft to be towed had its nose-, or tail-wheel lifted on to a small platform and secured. The handler in use today is a further development of this type.

The Mechanical Handler Mk 1, also known colloquially as the Mini-horse, or Donkey, was a three-wheeled chassis mounting a 3.6hp Coventry

A Victor towbar in use, along with an oxygen trolley, at
RAF Waddington, 24 March 1990.

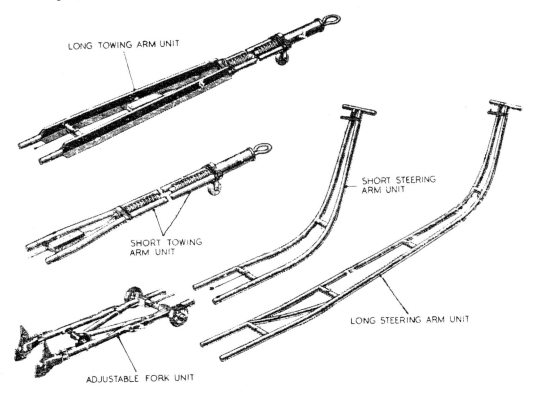

LONG TOWING ARM UNIT

SHORT TOWING
ARM UNIT

ADJUSTABLE FORK UNIT

SHORT STEERING
ARM UNIT

LONG STEERING ARM UNIT

The steering arm and tail assemblies consist of an adjustable fork unit, two steering-arm units and two towing-arm units.
The fork unit is adjustable to give a range of widths and can be combined with any one of the steering or towing-arm
units to form a tail-steering, or towing, arm suitable for aircraft up to 20,000lb (9072kg) AUP. Used mainly for naval or
Fleet Air Arm units.

A Land-rover of 5FTS of RAF Oakington towing a Vampire at the satellite airfield of RAF Graveley in 1957. All suitable MT was brought into use in this period, when the Oakington runways were being refurbished.

A Beverley transport aircraft being hangared. This operation required the use of special side-movement 'skates'. The nose of the aircraft was jacked up to allow the fins and rudders to be lowered to clear the door frame and roof trusses. The photo also shows the type of towing tractor specially developed for these large aircraft (Ray Honeybone).

Victor air-cooled diesel engine which drove two pneumatically tyred rear wheels through a three-speed gearbox; the gears were not changeable on the move, being utilised as the lowest speed for the greatest weight, the highest for light or no loads. A tiller arm carrying the engine controls and steering a front, solid-tyred castor wheel also acted as a brake by up and down movement. The engine controls consisted of a squeeze lever rather like a bicycle brake handle which, when released automatically, cut the engine to idling revs and disengaged the clutch. At the rear a three-tier towing pintle was fitted and to give sufficient adhesion to the rear wheels solid cast weights were bolted to the rear chassis. The handler weighed in at 2542lb (1153kg).

The earlier marks of handler were universal in that they could also tow most mobile items fitted with eye and pintle. The handlers specifically designed to tow aircraft were the Mk 5 and 5A. They worked by applying a friction roller to the tread of one of the aircraft's main wheels through a hydraulic transmission drive and roller chains, driven as in the Mk 1 by an air-cooled diesel engine mounted on a three-wheel chassis. A gate mechanism swung open the front roller to permit the positioning of the handler at the aircraft wheel,

the rear-driving roller controlled the forward movement and the front roller the rearward movement of the aircraft. Engine operation and hydraulic power and brakes were controlled from a control arm fitted to the rear wheel for steering, and auxiliary wheels were fitted to the chassis for raising the handler off the ground to allow free movement when not engaged in towing. For steering the aircraft under tow, a separate steering arm was attached to the nose- or tail-wheel. The difference in marks was that the 5 had a 12V system and the 5A a 24/28V system. Weight was 3640lb (1650kg).

A later and more sophisticated development, the type EN, dispensed with the friction drive by having a remote-controlled clamp-lift mechanism which clasped the nose wheel of such aircraft as the Phantom or Harrier, lifting it and enabling the aircraft to be towed, pushed and steered from that point. This model is driven by electric motor from six 12V 178amp/hr batteries and can be adapted, by the use of accessories, to tow or be used as a forklift; it can also be used as a jacking system for wheel changing. The driver/operator retains full control through a combined control tiller arm to

Mk I Mechanical Handler (Mini-horse). This pedestrian-controlled vehicle is used for towing ground equipment up to 15 tons in weight. It consists of a three-wheeled chassis on which a Coventry Victor AD 3.6hp air-cooled diesel engine provides the drive to two rear wheels via a three-speed/reverse gearbox and differential unit. Transmission is through an automatic centrifugal clutch. Steering is controlled by a pivoted tiller arm on the front wheel and incorporates the throttle control squeeze lever which, when released, reduces engine speed to a tick-over and automatically disengages the clutch. Hydraulic brakes on the rear wheels are applied by the tiller. A three-tier towing pintle is fitted.

An ML Aviation Mechanical Handler Mk 1 moving the rather weighty Simon Topper hydraulic servicing platform on what appears to be RAF Cottesmore *(ML Aviation Co. Ltd)*.

engage and lift, reposition, lower and disengage from the arm. A number of safety factors are built in whereby the handler cannot be moved under power if;

> The canopy is raised handbrake is ON
> Main brakes are ON when the batteries are on charge.

The handler is capable of moving up to 12,000lb (5443kg) nose- or tail-wheel weight.

Mechanical Aircraft Handler MK5 and 5A. These units operate by applying a friction roller drive to the tread of one of the aircraft main wheels. Each consists of a three-wheeled chassis on which is mounted a Coventry Victor HDA air-cooled diesel engine for driving the friction rollers and two front wheels through a hydraulic transmission drive and roller chains. A control arm carries the steering, engine hydraulic mechanism and braking controls. A gate mechanism swings open the front roller to position the handler at the aircraft wheel; the rear driving roller controls forward movement, the front roller controls rearward movement. The Mk 5 has a 12V system, the Mk 5A a 24/28V system.

David Brown tractor type VIG 1 (1941–44), used for towing aircraft, bomb carriers, etc. It was equipped with a 37hp engine with low-speed gearbox. A winch was fitted and some later types had fluid-drive torque converters *(David Brown Ltd)*.

An ML Aviation aircraft handler type EN doing the job for which it was originally designed – towing a carrier-borne aircraft, in this case a Buccaneer. This mark of handlers was battery-powered *(ML Aviation Co. Ltd)*.

An ML Aviation aircraft handler in use for helicopter work. The aircraft, a Lynx, is secured against movement by a special restraint system on board HMS *Sirius (ML Aviation Co. Ltd)*.

ML Aviation Mk 1 handler, also known in the RAF as the Mini-horse on servicing at RAF St Athan in June 1986. The control arm at the front is padlocked in the 'off' position for safety reasons.

A type EN2 Mechanical Handler awaiting disposal after refurbishing at RAF Stafford, 20 October 1993.

An ML Aviation Coolair MK 7 unit being moved by that company's pedestrian-operated aircraft handler. The handler can tow many other units, in addition to aircraft. The aircraft shown is a Comet of Transport Command *(ML Aviation Co. Ltd)*.

Once the aeroplane had been pushed or towed into the required position, if it was to fly, the next major operation was to start its engine(s).

Although they came under the control of Motor Transport, a brief mention of some of the tractors which have been used for towing might not come amiss. The first, other than the experimental Clayton, was the venerable Fordson, which was used extensively before and through WW2. American Case tractors were supplied under lend-lease, but were, in general, rather too large – most found their way to the Middle East theatre. The David Brown tractors came into the RAF during the WW2 years and ranged from the 1941–44 VIG, which was primarily designed for the job and powered by a 37hp petrol engine; the 1948–56 Taskmaster, which was developed from an agricultural model, as was the original Fordson, and had a six-speed gearbox and later, a fluid-drive torque converter; to the 1952–58 VIG series, specifically designed for heavy towing. Today, towing is done by such MT as the massive Tugmaster for the heaviest aircraft and the Massey Ferguson MF40, a light but powerful custom-built tractor in use for towing Tornado aircraft and similar weights.

David Brown tractor type VIG (1952–58) for towing aircraft. A heavy-duty version of the Taskmaster, powered by a 30hp petrol engine fitted with a fluid-drive torque converter. Some models were fitted with a rear-mounted winch *(David Brown Ltd)*.

An American Lend-Lease Case tractor in use at RAF Fayid in 1949. Quite a large machine, it was not used very much in the UK.

A modern Tugmaster-type tractor pushing a Lockheed L-1011-500 TriStar. More and more aircraft are being pushed rather than towed, as the tractor driver has better visibility and more control over the operation. Manchester Airport, 22 February 1993.

A Massey Ferguson MF 40 light aircraft-towing tractor in July 1987 at RAF Cottesmore, where it is used for towing Tornados. The multi-jaw towing hitch fitted to front and rear is to accommodate variation of towbar height. Full safety lighting is provided.

Massey Ferguson MF 40 tractor towing a GAF/Luftwaffe Tornado at RAF Cottesmore, July 1987.

Chapter 3

Starting

Ranged in a ragged line alongside four flapping Bessoneau hangars, six DH9A of B Flight faced towards the muddy, cheerless airfield, their wings rocking in the gusty wind, wheels chocked fore and aft, air mechanics hovering around, waiting for the aircrew. The skies were grey and cold, matching the air of tired, near apathy, bred from the passing of the cruel, relentless winter. It was April 1918.

A stir, and the pilots and gunners trooped out from the squadron hut, one or two making jokes, others grim and silent. The pilots climbed into the waiting aircraft and, after settling themselves and securing their safety belts, each went through the time-honoured drill of starting the big Liberty engines.

With a mechanic on the propeller the starting drill went thus:

Mechanic: 'Switches orf, suck in.'
Pilot: 'Switches off, suck in.' Checks switches are off, puts fuel cock on, opens throttle slightly.

With the calibre of recruit the RFC/RAF attracted, the accent on 'orf/off' might well be reversed.

Mechanic pulls the prop round a couple of times as pilot operates the hand fuel pump. Mechanic places prop on compression in a horizontal position and calls out:

'Switches on, Contact.'
Pilot: 'Switches on, Contact.' Puts throttle lever partly open, puts switches to on.

Mechanic then gives a heave to pull the prop hard enough to, hopefully, make the engine fire, making sure he is moving well clear of it when and should it do so.

If the engine does not fire he calls out:

'Switches off.'
Pilot: 'Switches off.' Puts switches to off, closes throttle.

Mechanic places prop on compression again and the drill is repeated for swinging on contact; it is continued until the engine fires, the mechanic is exhausted or a fault is assumed.

If, as a result of constant trying, the mixture became too rich, the drill was to 'blow out' the rich mixture from the cylinders in order to start again with the correct fuel. The switches were put to off, the fuel cock was closed and the throttle placed fully open, when the prop was then pulled back a few revolutions to clear the cylinders of the rich gas.

This essential starting charade was repeated at each aircraft until, if possible, all engines were running. The air gunners, if not aboard, then emplaned and the engines were run to warm up the oil. When warm the pilots signalled their mechanics to the rear of the aircraft to hold down the tail, while the pilot opened the throttle to maximum revs to check magnetos and oil pressure. Once he was satisfied, he would allow the revs to drop, the mechanics moved clear and the pilots waved chocks away.

Aerodromes were usually rather small behind the Western Front and the pilots, after waving off the mechanics at the wing-tips were soon, with bursts of engine, at the take-off point. Some jockeying for position, final checks for any aircraft on the approach and they were off for yet another offensive patrol behind the enemy lines. All this was routine. For the mechanics, the routine was to service machines on check routines or to repair damaged aircraft.

The starting procedure detailed above was to remain, in essence, the basic method for many years, with starting drill being taught as a normal feature of technical training for tradesmen closely connected with aircraft operations, up to 1947. This was especially true for the pre-war non-technical trade of Aircrafthand (General Duties) who were often detailed for prop swinging. By 1917 the RFC

Three airmen at a pre-war RAF station demonstrate the three-man-chain method of swinging the propeller to start the Rolls-Royce engine of a Bristol fighter (MOD H695).

and RNAS had adapted the front ends of old fuselages to become training rigs for teaching starting drill. Other methods of starting were evolved as a result of development and new techniques over the years, which can be grouped roughly into five groups:

Group 1	Hand swinging of the propeller.
Group 2	Hucks starter, handle and gas starting.
Group 3	Trolley accumulator.
Group 4	Cartridge start.
Group 5	Mechanical, electrical and air-operated ground power units (GPUs) and starter trolleys.

Groups 1, 3 and 4 were somewhat minimal in equipment requirements, Group 4 being short-lived.

Group 2 began the specialist GSE that was to become Group 5 and one of great profusion.

The early in-line aircraft engines were based on the automobile engines in current use and, including the rotary and radial types, were all of very low horsepower. It was, therefore, quite easy, after priming the engine with petrol, to start it by swinging the propeller by hand to turn the crankshaft and so operate the magneto. Hand starting bumbled along quite happily until WW1 when, as with all other aspects of aviation, engine development was accelerated under the impetus of that vicious war. Engine power increased rapidly, particularly with the in-line types such as Rolls-Royce, Sunbeam, Wolseley, Hispano Suiza, reaching 400hp with the American Packard Liberty in the DH9A. To obtain this power, cylinder compression, number of cylinders and revolutions were increased, which made the turning over of engines by hand via the propeller much harder, but handling the compression was still deemed to be within the capabilities of a trained mechanic, with the exception of the Liberty, which really required the linking

Starting the Bentley rotary engine of a Sopwith Snipe with the famous Hucks starter, early 1920s–mid 1930s. A major advance in the starting of high-powered engines, the Hucks was built on to a Ford car chassis *(MOD H691)*.

strength of two men to pull the propeller against compression. Manpower was plentiful, but the short answer was that there was still no easier method available.

Air mechanics were not enamoured of starting engines by this method, not only because of the hard work involved but because of the inherent dangers from which there had been serious injuries. Prop kickback, misheard starting drill or cockpit finger trouble, which was not uncommon, could cause accidents, and cases were also known of erks losing their footing on the swing or not getting out of the way of the firing propeller quickly enough and getting messily roughed up. The majority of engines were hand swung, but a few, such as the Rolls-Royce engines in the Handley Page 0/100, had handles and fewer still were started by compressed air bottles. The Sunbeam engines in the Short seaplanes fell into

this category – understandably, as they were water-borne. Although some attempts were made to alleviate the dangers of hand starting, it was obvious that this state of affairs could not go on and more efficient methods of starting had to be found.

The advent of the more powerful engines increased the incentive to make the natural manpower starting drill more efficient. Two men were now needed, one gripping the prop blade, the second helping to pull and most importantly, to drag No. 1 clear as the engine fired. The engines of such aircraft as the DH9A's 400hp Liberty, Avro Aldershot, Rolls-Royce Condor's 600hp, the 450hp of the Atlas and the Wapiti's 550hp Jupiter were of too high a compression for two men and a 'chain' gang of three and four men was introduced. No. 1 of the chain required a strong grip, as he faced the engine; No. 2 faced the opposite way (usually forward) to ensure maximum wrist grip, with No. 3 and No. 4, if used, facing alternately.

A derivative of the chain-gang method was to use a strong rope to which was attached a canvas bag; this was placed on a vertical blade on compression

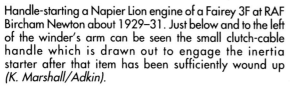

Handle-starting a Napier Lion engine of a Fairey 3F at RAF Bircham Newton about 1929–31. Just below and to the left of the winder's arm can be seen the small clutch-cable handle which is drawn out to engage the inertia starter after that item has been sufficiently wound up (K. Marshall/Adkin).

Hand-starting the Rolls-Royce Kestrels of a Handley Page Heyford at RAF Worthy Down in the summer of 1937. The picture shows how the handle-winding energy is trans-mitted through rods and gears to the engine.

and the rope was pulled by the gang. The main value of this method was the safety factor; when the large prop kicked over on firing, all the swingers were well clear. Prop swinging carried on well into the 1930s – and with light aircraft, well into the post-war years.

The famous Hucks starter, the first piece of real mobile ground equipment for this operation, was designed in 1916 by an officer of that name, but did not enter service until the early 1920s. It was the largest single improvement to spare the airmen much of the physical chore in swinging the props and gave a greater number of first-time starts. It could be said to be the first of the present trend of mobile engine starters. This much revered mechanical machine was built on a model T Ford chassis and comprised a semi-universal shaft, mounted on a framework bolted to lie fore and aft and above the car chassis, driven by a chain from the car engine through a clutch. A crosshead on the shaft engaged with a dog on the aircraft propeller boss and both automatically disengaged when the engine started. The section of the shaft carrying the crosshead was telescopically spring-loaded, which allowed the Hucks to be positioned well clear of the prop, and the shaft was semi-adjustable to allow for the varying heights and angles of prop shafts of most of

the single-engined aeroplanes for which it was primarily designed. The device was for aerodrome use only and with aircraft of the time having no brakes it was essential that the aircraft was securely chocked. It is possible that the Hucks may have served overseas, but it became a familiar sight on most UK aerodromes during the mid 1920s to early 1930s. The Hucks operator was an MT driver. This versatile machine is still in use at Old Warden airfield for starting the Shuttleworth Collection of single-engined aircraft.

The second alternative in Group 2 was to turn over the engine(s) by handle(s). The mechanics of handle starting meant that physical strength was still required to turn engines against compression, in addition to the extra friction of any rods and gearing. It was still good for the biceps, though. During the development of starting systems several aircraft types utilised the handle as part of the method and many later aircraft retained the handle as an emergency, notably in France in 1939, where ground-starting equipment was not readily available on some airfields. The various methods included Eclipse, Rotax, Rolls-Royce, Inertia and direct electrical cranking. The minimum basic requirement of these methods was that the gear ratio between engine crankshaft and handle was low enough to allow one or two men to turn and give maximum

Pre-WW2 trolley accumulator on display at the Aerospace Museum at Cosford. Under the cover is a JAP single-cylinder petrol engine charging set. The iron wheels were changed for tyred ones to lessen the risk of fire from sparking.

A rather battered accumulator starter trolley still in use after about thirty years. Earlier models had a non-towing handle. This model was in use at Woodford aerodrome in June 1985.

possible speed at the engine crankshaft. A ratchet mechanism – or similar – was usually incorporated to prevent engines being cranked in the wrong direction, or preventing injury by backfire. A slipping clutch, usually of the disc and spring-loaded type, was normally fitted. The Eclipse and Rotax types were based on this standard with variations depending on the aircraft. Rotax introduced the direct cranking electrical starter, which applied the torque from an electrical motor direct to the engine crankshaft and which used a detachable handle (as did most types) for unsticking a cold engine, or for adjustment purposes.

The Handley Page Heyford was a good example of inbuilt mechanical friction into the starter system. The handle engagement fitted to a gear train at the top of the undercarriage structure and transmitted winding power by two sets of bevel gears and long shafts to the Kestrel engine mounted about 10ft (3m) above.

Some of the biplane types, such as the Armstrong Whitworth Atlas and Fairey 111F, Gordon and Swordfish, employed the inertia starter, which was based on a small flywheel with a steel rim and weighing about 6lb (2.7kg); it was accelerated to about 1200rpm via a handle-wound gear train – a ratio of about 150:1 from handle to flywheel – which gave 90–100 revs at the starting dog. When

maximum revs were reached by the winders, the starting dog was engaged with the engine crankshaft by a small cable-operated clutch – usually by another airman – and the initial energy released was transmitted via a reduction gearing to a multi-disc clutch. This method had one great disadvantage in that it was a one-shot device; if the engine did not fire, a lot of human energy was expended and the fitter in the cockpit, or the pilot, would be duly blasphemed – *sotto voce*. A later derivative of the method, welcomed by ground crews, was to use an electric motor to accelerate the flywheel. These systems were used a great deal on American aircraft such as the Douglas DC3, Skymaster, etc.

On some aircraft which employed direct cranking, such as the Avro Anson, it was also the job of the winder to charge the engine cylinders with sufficient raw fuel by the Ki-gas pump, as decided by the cockpit occupant, this was not always a clear-cut decision but the pace of war-training establishments, operating each of these aircraft around four sorties a day every day, proved it to be reliable, if hard graft.

When the Expansion programme introduced the new breed of monoplane fighters, those powered by the Rolls-Royce Merlin, the Hurricane, Spitfire and Defiant, light bombers Battle and Henley, together with the RR Kestrel used in the Hart and Fury variants, used starting-handle systems of a common design for these engines. The type had Bendix drive, which was a form of engagement of an eight-toothed starter jaw pinion to engine crankcase by screw thread. Full engagement of the jaw on the thread was taken up before the engine turned over. Roller gear was fitted to prevent kickback on backfire. On engagement an electric motor was brought into operation to provide starting current, which could be operated by the aircraft's batteries in lieu of the handle, and often was.

The largest multi-engined biplanes, service and civilian, usually had their engines mounted on struts between the wings which, combined with their height above the ground, made it difficult to reach the propellers, so hand swinging was out. Gas starting required the use of a separate system built into the engine system, which utilised air stored under pressure in a bottle and supplied from an external source, in conjunction with petrol from the aircraft's tanks, fed under control to an atomiser, which was similar in operation to a carburettor. There it was mixed with the pressure air to a combustible charge and was directed, still under pressure, to the engine cylinders. The pressure caused the pistons to operate, so turning the engine. A hand magneto was wound and (usually) after a couple of turns the engine fired and the main magneto and carburettor came into operation. A derivative of this system was to use a small two-stroke petrol engine – another piece of ground equipment – to drive a compressor in conjunction with a vaporiser to feed fuel into the cylinders. It was used at first only on main aerodromes and probably by the civil airlines, but modified versions of the system were later tried for some single-engined and multi-engined RAF aircraft.

Starting by handle was an enforced condition in the relatively leisurely years of peace, but for war the slowness of starting by this method could not be considered, particularly for fighters. Handles were used extensively in the later weeks of the war in France, when all was chaos and equipment a luxury; under such conditions the handle proved its use. But on the static airfields of the Battle of Britain, where interceptor patrols were continually required, the method was too slow and exhausting for rapid scrambles. The solution was provided by the introduction of the trolley accumulator.

A possible originator of the services Accumulator Starting Trolley Mk 5 was the Dagenite battery

The Merlin 35 of a Balliol T2 trainer of 7 FTS RAF Cottesmore in 1953, being started by what is possibly a Mk 5 trolley accumulator, which was also used for similar light-piston aircraft such as Beaver and Jet Provost (C.C.H.Cole).

trolley, made by Peto and Radford and introduced in 1936 for civil airline use. It closely resembled the later RAF model, consisting basically of a four-wheeled hand-pulled/pushed steerable chassis on which was mounted a two-compartment wood container, one compartment housing two high-capacity 6V 17amp/hr batteries at ten hour rate of discharge. The other compartment held the feeder cable. Its price then was £22.15.0 (£22.75).

The first RAF trolley acc followed the Peto and Radford design, comprising a battery box with lid and holding four 6V batteries, mounted on an angle-iron chassis fitted with a tee handle, two large all-iron wheels and a smaller wheel under the handle. Projecting from a junction box was a heavy-duty rubber-protected feeder cable about 15ft (4.6m) long with a two-pin brass plug for insertion into the aircraft's starting socket. The trolley acc remained in this basic form throughout its service life, with a few necessary modifications. This one form of starting, with which practically all RAF service tradesmen and women from 1938 on are familiar, is still in service on some smaller jet aircraft and almost all the RAF's remaining piston-engined aircraft.

All that was required of the ground crew was to see that the aircraft was safely chocked, trolley acc was plugged into the aircraft system and all was clear for starting. When the pilot or fitter gave the 'thumbs up' signal, the airman on the trolley acc pressed the start button. The cockpit occupant then went through the starting drill and, if the trolley acc was in good condition, it was seldom the engine failed to start, finger trouble excepting.

Because of the rapid rate of exhaustion of the accumulator batteries from the harsh demands of the larger engines, resulting in a high stock of batteries held under charge, the trolley acc was quickly modified to accept a 24V charging set, powered by a small two-stroke JAP engine, the whole mounted on an extension of the chassis frame. Other models that followed incorporated towing handles instead of a tee, a towing hook and, at last, rubber-tyred wheels. The first tyres were of a popular car size and within a few months they showed a phenominal rate of wear! This only decreased when a bastard-size tyre was introduced. A Triumph-engined model was introduced in 1947 for hangar use, fitted with a manual advance and retard lever which was the cause of a few broken wrists when being started from wrong setting of the lever. In these various forms the starters were used throughout the war and after, all over the Allied world, and more than proved their worth.

During the post-WW2 years the Western world was living in some tension with the Eastern bloc – the so-called Cold War – and the V bombers had become a first line of attack. The absolute minimum possible of just over four minutes for scrambling these aircraft on receipt of a Red Alert was critical. To this end the saving of seconds in the overall start time

Electrical Starting and Servicing Trolley 12/50kW Mk 3 and 4. Among the first of the 'tarmac' units, these machines reflect the starting trolley design of the period, before the advent of electronics; with a weight of over 10,000lb (4535 kg), they are 'bridge' built to last. They were powered by either an IC engine – the MK 3 – or an electric motor – the Mk 4. Both were much in use and both were comprehensively equipped with control panel and instrumentation. The chassis was fitted with overrun brake; the whole unit was weather screened and needed an MT prime mover to move it.

was vital and the trolley accs were found to be insufficiently powerful for a sustained start of four engines in about one minute. The ground crews had already got the emergency starting drill down to its lowest factor and the time loss was mainly due to the fact that each engine had to be started separately. Could it be possible to start all four engines at once? It could and was.

The Simstart Trolley Mk 1, types 1A, 1B and 1C, was the invention of an officer of that name (Sim, in the Hucks tradition) and the three types, although basically similar in design and construction, were not interchangeable. The 1A was for Vulcan use, the 1B for Victor and the 1C for Valiant, each clearly marked with that aircraft name and each provided with the necessary starter-control circuit and electrical power for the simultaneous starting of all four engines. Each trolley was virtually a super-size trolley acc, having a bank of twenty-one batteries, together with starter, control and distribution panels and associated wiring. The twenty-one 24V 40amp/hr type H lead acid batteries were arranged, one for the normal 24V supply to starter and control panels and twenty in banks of five, all enclosed; all could be recharged from a new standard 112/12V supply electrical servicing trolley. The Simstart was a special product for a particular job; it worked efficiently, but was replaced when a succession of new type electrical starter trolleys entered service.

Electric Starting Trolley Accumulator Mk 5. A late development of the standard trolley accumulator, this Mk 5 is modified for use on 24V d/c supply for starting aircraft turbine engines requiring steady current loads of 200–600 amps. This mark has four 6V accumulators of 230 amp capacity, connected in series to provide 24V. The battery container, with appropriate controls and lead, is mounted on a three-wheel chassis designed for towing.

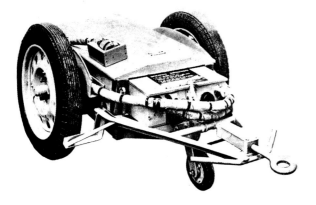

The Simstart Trolley Mk 1, Types 1A, 1B and 1C. These Class 1 trolleys were introduced to provide the power for the simultaneous starting of all four engines of the V-class bomber aircraft and were produced in three variants, specialist to each aircraft type. They were basically similar, varying only in starter panel and associated wiring. The example shown is a type 1A, for the Avro Vulcan; types 1B and 1C were for the Handley Page Victor and Vickers Valiant respectively.

The trolley accumulators were suitably modified and used for the early jet engines, but as these gas turbines became more powerful so a different form of external starting, as mentioned above, began to supersede the venerable trolley acc. The new starters were first known as Ground Power Units (GPUs) and later as Electrical Servicing and Starter Trolleys. But before they came into almost universal use the cartridge starter had its brief period of service.

During the years following the introduction of the jet engine into the RAF, when the thrust of these engines was increasing rapidly, the greater mass weight of the Avon and Sapphire engines in the Hunter, Javelin and Canberra meant that, while the free-running turbine and compressor could be spun with a finger, a high-powered unit was needed to supply the energy to spin it to the starting revolutions for which the electrical starters had been evolved. However, in the 1950s and 1960s, fast turn round by the fighter aircraft, plus the bonus of keeping flight decks clear of potentially dangerous and unwelcome bulky gear, had led the Royal Navy aircraft to be specified where necessary the use of the Coffman cartridge starter system. This was based on the use of a special cartridge, fired in an equally special breech capable of holding several cartridges, the rapid expansion of the hot gases being utilised to operate a piston geared to turn over the large turbine engines very rapidly indeed. The cartridge starters were used on early Hunters, Javelins and Canberras primarily to reduce the need for trolley accs. A later

Lightweight Low-Pressure Air Starting Trolley Mk II. A lightweight mobile unit mounted on a four-wheeled chassis designed to supply air at 2lb/sec at 40lb/sq. in (0.907kg at 2.812kg/sq. cm). It was used for starting turbine-engined aircraft in the 1960s.

development of these starters was the Isopropylene system (AUPIN) which was fitted to the later Hunter fighters.

The method was found reasonably successful in these aircraft and was very useful in giving them the ability to self-start away from base. There were snags with the system, of course; cases occurred of cartridges misfiring in the breech, somewhat to the detriment of the breech and the fitter/pilot's nerves. Larger engines required more powerful cartridges, but, despite a period when practically the whole of the Western powers' naval aircraft used the system, it was found that too much stress was being put on the larger turbines by the almost explosive force required to spin them quickly to the starting revs; the system was eventually dropped. For historical interest, one of the first users of the cartridge starting was the DH Chipmunk, a small trainer/ communication aircraft introduced into the RAF in 1950.

From the mid 1950s began the use of a variety of the new electrical starter and servicing units, made by names which were soon synonymous with reliability under all service conditions. As to their effectiveness

An early Murex ground power unit, later known as an electrical starting and servicing trolley, 12/50kW, being used to start a Fairey FD1 research delta wing aircraft at the 1955 SBAC Display *(Murex)*.

in relieving the workload of the tradesmen, that is a moot point, open for discussion; they were certainly instrumental in the eventual forming of a new trade for the sole purpose of maintaining them. Among the first units into service were the Murex GPUs designed for such aircraft as the V bombers, the transports Britannia, Comet and Andover, etc.

These first GPUs tended to be made in pairs, one independent of hangar power supply for use on dispersal areas and the other dependent on mains supply. Both resultant functions were the same, that of supplying electrical power for the servicing of an aircraft's electrical system and radio/radar equipment – its prime function – and the starting of engines.

The Murex Mk 3 and 4 12/50kW trolleys illustrate the trend in design of early 'tarmac' types, being of rugged bridge-built type construction, before the extensive use of electronics transformed the weight factor. The Mk 3 was powered by a Rolls-Royce B81 Mk 5G petrol engine to drive a 12/50kW dual-voltage generator, which provided simultaneous sources of power, one of 28V 12kW and the other of 112V 50kW. A comprehensive control panel for electrical and engine operation was mounted above the generator on anti-vibration mountings. The

Mk 4 was basically similar, but powered by an electric screened slip ring induction motor of 100hp, 2500rpm, three-phase 50 cycle continuous rating and designed for hangar use.

In addition to full electrical characteristics the trolleys had full fault protection, with the electrical equipment mounted on a fabricated steel trailer chassis with four double wheels and protected by a steel-hinged canopy with detachable panels. Brakes were fitted to the front wheels only, operated either by an overrun device or a handwheel on the side of the trailer. The weight of the trolleys reflected the strength of their construction, a massive 9324lb (4230kg), requiring the use of a powered prime mover. The trolleys were 12ft (3.7m) long, 7ft (2.13m) wide and 6ft 9in (2.06m) high.

Although designed for use on the heavy bomber aircraft, these GPUs were too heavy and bulky for fast turn-round work and their use gave those working on the line more physical problems. No longer could an airman grab one, like a trolley acc, and trundle it to the aircraft with little effort; it was now often necessary to find, or have attached, a prime mover, usually a tractor, to move this dead weight. It was the beginning of the 'tarmac clutter' that was to build progressively over the succeeding years and to require the attention of specialist trades to maintain it.

In the natural course of development and with the increasing use of electronics leading to micro-electronics, the size and weight of succeeding GPUs and

A Houchin 25kVA model 585 ground power unit *(Houchin publicity photograph)*.

A Houchin 28V d/c model 641 ground power unit for servicing electrical systems and starting engines. The GPU is powered by a Perkins six-cylinder diesel engine *(Houchin publicity photograph)*.

electrical starter and servicing trolleys came down conversely with their efficiency going up and becoming more compact. Instead of paired items of the Murex type, one starter was designed to supply power independently for both starting and servicing the electrical systems, with the main emphasis on the latter, but the paired starters remained in service for many years and, in fact, are still in use. An example of the lighter type was manufactured by Houchin and has a dual output of 200V ac three phase, 400cps at 15kVA and 28V dc at 10kW. A Ford series 209E six cylinder in-line, water-cooled petrol engine or a 45hp electric motor drive a brushless ac generator and a compound wound dc generator at 3000rpm. The electric motor operates from a 415V, three-phase, 50cps mains supply. The generators, power unit and control panel are mounted on a four-wheel trailer chassis, enclosed by canopy and panels and fitted with storage lockers. An overrun/parking brake is fitted. The modern Houchin types in the 60kVA range are comprehensively designed for ease of access for servicing and maintenance (as the photo on page 47 shows) and are fully instrumented, which has led to the need for a somewhat lengthy starting and operating drill when using these trolleys.

Running parallel to the introduction and use of the electrical starting and servicing trolleys are the

low-pressure air starters, which became standard
engine starters. This method adapted the principle
of the gas turbine engine itself to provide low-pressure air from a small air turbine acting
independently as a starter motor. The method was
much less explosive than the cartridge start but,
following true to type, there was soon an assorted
variety of these starters designed by the specialist
firms and accepted into the RAF. Most of these
firms were producing both the electrical start and
service trolleys and the gas turbine starters: Auto
Diesel, Houchin, ML Aviation, Petbow and Bristol
Siddeley, to name a few.

The air-start method came into use in the 1960s,
requiring more GSE than the cartridge start, and the
early Low Pressure Air Starter Trolley Mk 4 is an
example of the pattern of these machines. This one
was designed for multi-engined aircraft, proving
extremely useful in taking over from the Simstart,
and comprised a Palouste Mk 104 air bleed gas
turbine mounted in a centrally positioned cradle on
the trolley chassis between two 18½ gallon (84 litre)
fuel tanks. The Palouste provided a bleed flow of 2lb
(0.907kg) air per second at 38psi (2.67kg/sq. cm)
pressure. Mounted at the top was a storage rack for
the air delivery hoses and electrical lead, compart-
ments each side accommodated two 24V batteries
and trolley accessories. The trolley chassis was

A Houchin 35kW electrical starter used at RAF Leeming,
showing cable stowages and control panel. November
1986 (A. Eaton/Adkin).

The control panel for a Houchin model 680 60kVa ground
power unit's Cummins diesel engine on site at RAF
Cottesmore in June 1980 (RAF Official AC427 G2).

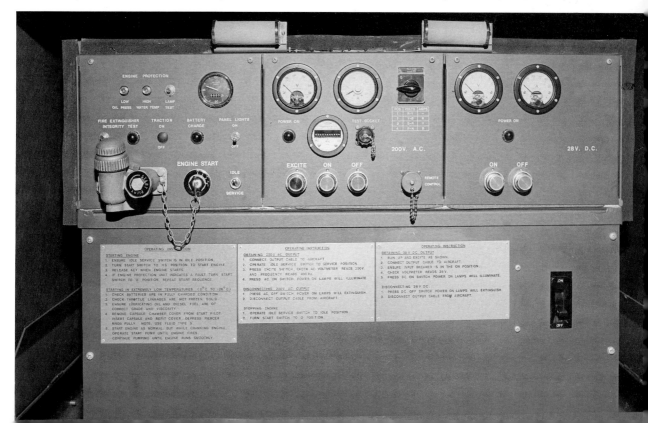

mounted on two pneumatic-tyred wheels, had a retractable castor wheel fitted to the towbar and was fitted with an overrun parking brake. Weight was 2025lb (919kg). The air delivery hose and electrical control leads were connected from the trolley to the aircraft point and the trolley started and run at idling speed, when its operation became semi-

automatic, leaving the engine starting under the control of either the aircraft's pilot or the starter operator.

The operational control panel of a Houchin model 680 60kVa ground power unit in use at RAF Cottesmore in June 1987 *(RAF Official 3959 G1)*.

 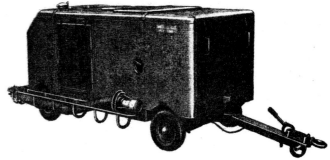

Low-Pressure Air Starting Trolley Mk 4. A bleed flow of 2lb (0.9kg) per sec at 38.5psi (2.70kg/sq. cm) pressure is provided by a Palouste Mk 104 gas turbine mounted on the trolley chassis between two 18½-gallon (84-litre) tanks and fitted with air intake and exhaust silencers. The unit is totally enclosed. With hose and leads connected and the trolley at idling speed the operation is semi-automatic and starting is controlled by the aircraft pilot. The unit is fully roadworthy for towing.

Low-Pressure Air Starting Trolley Mk 12 and 12A. Of similar use to the Mk 4 above, this unit is mounted on a four-wheeled chassis comprising a STAD A1250 Mk 12 or 12A single-stage gas turbine with a 50-gallon (228-litre) fuel tank and controls. The trolley is fully enclosed and has an instrument and control panel in the canopy. The Mk 12A incorporates a dump valve operated automatically by pressure in the air casing.

Flight line crewman plugging in an electrical starter trolley to a Dominie of the Air Electronics and Air Engineers School at RAF Finningley in May 1984 (Ron Phillips, RAF Official).

Low-pressure air starter Mk 4 with a Palouste 104 gas turbine engine. This mark was used on the Vulcan prior to the introduction of the Simstart (page 44), but was also in general use. The latest mark in service is the Mk 12–12A. RAF Stafford, November 1986.

A Mk 12L Auto Diesel low-pressure air starter trolley at RAF Stafford in November 1986. The unit is air-transportable.

A low-pressure air starter trolley Mk 12A, showing the exhaust chute opened when the unit is in use. RAF Leeming, November 1986 (A. Eaton/Adkin).

The control panel of an Auto Diesel Mk 12A low-pressure air starting trolley at RAF Leeming in November 1986 (A. Eaton/Adkin).

A lightweight Mk II version was introduced in the mid-1960s for starting a number of gas turbines together from a delivery volume of 0.907kg per second at 40psi (2.81kg/sq. cm). Hose and lead were mounted on top of the starter and all controls were easy to hand. Weight was 900lb (408kg) and the four-wheeled chassis was towable. The latest of a long line, the Auto Diesel Mk 12-12A Low Pressure Air Starting Trolley follows similar principles and also uses its air pressure for 'motoring', or free running, engines during servicing or inhibiting. Of conventional appearance, the trolley has a STAD A1250 LK 12 or 12A single-stage inward-flow gas turbine with a 50 gallon (229 litre) fuel tank mounted on a four-wheel chassis; it is fully enclosed by detachable panels. An instrument and control panel is mounted at the rear and a flexible air hose, through which compressed air bled from the turbine is fed at approximately 25lb/sq. in (1.758kg/sq. cm) is stowed in a low-level trough. The Mk 12A incorporates a dump valve operated automatically by pressure in the air casing. Weight of the trolley is 3052lb (1386kg).

The Mk 12/12A presents some rather time-absorbing problems in the number of steps required to start and operate: before any attempt was made to operate the starter there were four warnings to observe and three cautions to check. To prepare the trolley for starting, twenty operations had to be carried out. Just prior to starting, a further two warnings had to be observed and on starting three operations and six sub-operations (notes) had to be done. After starting, six gauges and six lamps were checked for satisfactory performance.

The interior of a Mk 12L low-pressure air starter trolley taken from the left-hand side, showing the exhaust. RAF Stafford, November 1986.

The interior of a Mk 12L low-pressure air starter trolley taken from the right-hand side, showing the intake and engine installation. RAF Stafford, November 1986.

After taking ear-defender precautions, starting an engine from the LP starter required six operations; a cockpit-controlled start required seven. Normal shutdown of the trolley-power unit needed four operations only.

The trolley also had to be towed to and from the particular aircraft. Of course, much of this drill would come naturally – to some – by experience, but it is many operation sequences away from the 'old-fashioned' trolley acc's 'insert plug and press button'.

Perhaps all this time-consuming work, plus the proliferation of GPUs and electrical and air-pressure starting trolleys, which contributed to the general tarmac clutter of major airfields, influenced the acceptance of Auxiliary Power Units (APUs).

Although not strictly ground equipment, these units were developed as a means of reliable starting on airfields where GSE was minimal. They were originally fitted in service aircraft and were accepted into general use when the Boeing 727 entered service with them as general equipment fitted in the rear of the aircraft. In addition to being a source of on-board power with development they became a source of power also for aircraft cooling and heating purposes.

The APUs were developed into two main categories, high-pressure gas turbines for heavy/large aircraft and low-pressure gas turbines for light aircraft and helicopters, and are extensively used.

Chapter 4

Access

'Arbuthnot, get up and check the aileron control run in the top port wing of 62, the pilot complained of stiffness when doing a steep turn to port.' AC2 Arbuthnot, newest rigger to A Flight, stared up at the collection of vast planes, struts and wires that made up Handley Page 0/400 B8805 and thought, 'Hell, how do I get up there?'

That task, in 1918, was one of ladders tactically placed and firmly secured. Special long ones, suitably padded, were leaned against the top leading edge of the port mainplane and for safety's sake held at their base by another airman when required. The aircraft's wheels were firmly chocked fore and aft. Up the 20-odd feet climbed our intrepid air mechanic to discover on reaching the top the first rule of high-altitude servicing – take up to the job more than you might need rather than less. So, down

An Indian Air Force Ouragon at the staging post of RAF Mauripur in 1953 with the bare essentials of GSE: one pair of GP ladders and a trolley accumulator (J. Hughes).

he came to collect the required items. From his vantage point aloft he saw the huge shape of the aircraft in all its awesomeness, the mainplanes stretching out each side almost into the distant hangar sides, or so it seemed. The ladder he was on, and others of varying sizes as required, were the only means of access to such mechanical parts as he had been detailed, most of them buried within the fabric-covered planes. Ladders, therefore, were a prime item of servicing equipment and have remained so throughout the technical history of the RAF.

The five years after the Armistice of 1918 were a period of stabilisation after the staggering cost of the war, first in its needless loss of life, then in the countless millions spent on men and property. It was also a period of great reduction in manpower in the services, of which the RAF suffered to such an extent that it was almost eliminated as a fighting force. Those years fostered, in services and government, an understandable economic restraint which

was for many years to colour thinking to the point of obsession. A direct result was that for far too many of those years the RAF had to make do with WW1 aircraft and equipment.

The aircraft with which the RAF was equipped in 1918 had generally had a short operational life, but as the years passed the continuation of those few types in service depended on efficient maintenance to keep them flying, to compensate for the lack of new types. Fortunately from this point of view the biplanes of those days, although more complex to rig, and in some cases to assemble, were of simple construction. But by the very nature of its design an aeroplane needs to have easy access to its systems and replenishment points in the minimum time and using the minimum of equipment. With the comparative mechanical simplicity of the large biplanes, access usually meant either to the engines, to the fuel tanks or to the internals of top mainplanes and the control systems. Some of the larger twin-engined aircraft had access platforms built on to the engine-support struts or incorporated in the engine panels. For the rest the tradesmen relied on the ubiquitous wooden ladders in their various sizes.

First in line and destined to remain in continual use to the present day, from its humble beginning the stepladder was developed into some quite

'Who is it that keeps cluttering up the tarmac with all this equipment?' Hornets en route for Malaya stage through RAF Mauripur, 1953 (J. Hughes).

complex structures. Ladders of varying sizes were a must on most flying units; look into photographs of aircraft on the ground over the years and a pair of ladders will be lurking somewhere, if not in actual use. For very many years the ordinary wooden ladder was the main item of access equipment, and was generally adequate. On those large multi-engined biplanes standing high off the ground, with fuel tanks often contained in the top wing, a very long ladder was needed for refuelling access to the tanks which were usually in the centre section. This ladder stayed in service under the nomenclature of Ladder, Large Aircraft Refuelling, and was further developed into a telescopic type with a range of extensions from 14–17ft (4.3–5m), slightly braced and padded to prevent damage to the leading edges.

The ordinary stepladder group included the tall swingback types designed for individual heights of 6, 8, 12 and 14ft (1.8, 2.4, 3.6 and 4.2m); a small platform was incorporated at the top in some types. One particular ladder that was useful during the biplane era was a hinged type with staggered rungs which, when used in pairs and with a plank as a trestle, gave a good range of variable heights for wing removal/replacement in place of the standard gantry pillars (see Chapter 7).

The problem with most high-access jobs on aircraft was not the job itself but was the number of times a tradesman might have to climb up and down the ladder, first opening up access to the job, diagnosing any fault, collecting the necessary tools,

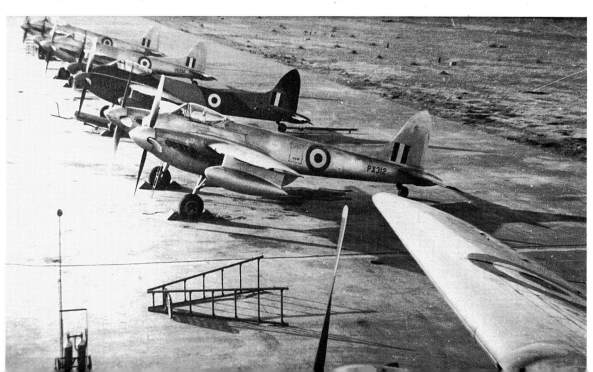

Fixed mobile GP flat-topped servicing ladders in the dump/dispersal area of the Aerospace Museum at Cosford in June 1985.

doing the work, getting an NCO to inspect the work and replacing panels and cowlings and fabric patches. And the arrival of NAAFI break. The present all-metal stepladders are flat-topped and classed as General Purpose type B. Earlier types were fitted with safety chains, later types have the chain removed, but some are fitted with small mobility wheels for when the ladder is folded. The increasing and varying heights of ladders required when the Expansion aircraft came into service made their use a continual hazard, coupled with their inadequacy and inability to hold any quantity of tools that might be required.

Ladders were also custom-designed for passenger use on transport aircraft, were strictly basic and functional, like those for the York and Hastings, but design veered to the eventual steps or stairs. With the increase in large passenger and freight aircraft the variation of sill heights was catered for by the Aircraft Entrance Ladder of the mid-1950s, which was adjustable for sill heights of 4–7ft (1.2–2.1m) by movement of one or more of the top treads. Two screw jacks were fitted to raise one end of the ladder to lift the mobility wheels and give a small degree of height adjustment to align the platform with the aircraft door sill. As the new transport aircraft increased in sophistication, so did the passenger

stairs, and those of the Edgehill type – used at Transport Command home and overseas bases – reflect the trend. These stairs had a sill height range from 5–11ft (1.5–3.3m), operated hydraulically. The step assembly and side panels were fitted with flush-mounted lighting operated from a 12V battery, together with fuse, switches and junction box. Rubber buffers were fitted to protect the aircraft and a towbar, rear wheel brakes and steady jacks for parking completed the specification. The ladder was further designed to be dismantled into sections for air transportation. Two examples of locally manufactured aircraft ladder/steps – in this case by 5MU – are shown. The larger appears to have been made from Dexion and angle strip and is complete with adjustable stabilising feet, mobility wheels and padding protection.

Variations developed on the ladder theme were those designed specifically for aircraft servicing, such as the Adjustable Flat Top Aircraft Servicing Ladder introduced in 1950, which had a working height of 8ft 5in (2.6m) adjustable from 7ft 2½in (2.2m) and was mounted on a metal frame to which were fitted two wheels and two retractable handles. This ladder was introduced for use on the Canberra tail unit and the theme was further developed by more sophisticated types, such as the Elevating and Extending Service Ladder Mk 2 and 3, introduced in the mid-1950s for servicing aero engines and external parts of an aircraft. The difference between the two marks was as follows: the Mk 2 was in two sections, which extended to a platform height of 17ft

A Britannia showing passenger stairs on the left and maintenance steps to the right. Duxford, July 1983.

A set of what may be locally made boarding steps ex-5MU – and quite nice, too – awaiting disposal at the Aerospace Museum at Cosford in June 1985. A Gloster Javelin is at the rear.

'Old' type airstairs not in general use but retained at Manchester Airport workshops until required. These stairs were also used by Transport Command. The top rear section is adjustable to increase stair height, and the unit is towable. July 1992.

A pair of locally made steps complete with adjustable (wind down) stabilising legs, utilised for both passengers and maintenance. The letters EMU stand for No.5 Maintenance Unit. RAF Cosford, February 1988.

(5.1m) from a minimum height of 8ft (2.4m) with a maximum platform overhang over the trailing wheels of 4ft 6in (1.37m); the Mk 3 was in three sections with a platform height of 32ft (9.7m) from a minimum height of 17ft (5.1m) with a maximum platform overhang of 9ft (2.7m). Operating controls were at ground level and both ladders were mounted on three-wheeled chassis fitted with screwed stabilising jacks. A towbar was also fitted.

The range of practical use of a ladder on aircraft servicing is very limited, although during the various

Adjustable Flat-top Aircraft Servicing Ladder. A portable ladder fitted with an adjustable height platform. The ladder chassis has retractable handles which are used after the unit has been wheeled into position. This ladder was designed for tail-unit servicing of the English Electric Canberra, but can be adapted to most situations.

Aircraft Engine Ladder. A ladder designed to give access to a range of aircraft with sill heights from 4ft 4in to 7ft 6in (1.3–2.3m) by moving the top treads to form a platform. Used in the 1950s and 1960s.

Elevating and Extending Aircraft Servicing Ladder Mk 2 & 3. This ladder was used in the 1950s mainly for aero-engine replacement but also to help the serviceman reach any external parts that were otherwise inaccessible. The Mk 2 was in two sections to give a maximum height of 17ft (5.1m), the Mk 3 is in three sections with a maximum platform height of 32ft (9.7m). The platforms also have overhang.

Edgehill Passenger Steps. Custom-built passenger-access steps fitted with rubber buffers, flush-mounted lights and a hydraulically operated step-elevation jacking system. The unit was towable and fitted with rear-wheel brakes with steady jacks for parking. The unit could be dismantled for transporting by air.

A gantry and swingback ladders are used in the erection of a replica Vimy F8614 Triple First in the RAF Hendon Museum, December 1983.

pre-war bush wars in which the RAF was involved ladders were sometimes the only pieces of access equipment in some squadrons. It was the new aircraft of the Expansion era that revealed the need for more suitable equipment, even if it took some years for this to reach fruition. First servicing platforms, for instance, were locally made, were of wood and heavy; they had 'wheelbarrow' handles but no wheels, although later versions were fitted with two wheels to allow them to be manoeuvred. The commercial units had a small ladder which gave access to a platform. After many years of service, and a few accidents from the breaking of oil-soaked wood, they were superseded by tubular steel types which were heavier and somewhat hernia-provoking to the poor old mechanic until some bright spark in the GSE halls of engineering heeded the fact that aluminium alloy tubing was lighter than mild steel. In general the height of these platforms varied slightly according to type of aircraft for which they were used. To offset the numbers required in service because of these variations, this type was eventually developed as an adjustable height platform, which became the progenitor of the Safety Raiser types.

Among the early all-metal commercial versions was the Inspection Platform type C, which had its platform adjustable in height from 5ft 6in to 8ft (1.7 to 2.4m) and was equipped with deep trays in the chassis frame, large cast-iron wheels and a towbar for mobility. Hand-operated clamps were used on the platform adjustable support tubes and on the four stabilising legs. Access to the platform was by a telescopic ladder and the weight of this GSE was 450lb (204kg). Two derivatives of this unit were the types N and M. The type N, introduced in 1950, was of steel tube open box construction and had a sloping ladder at its side which led to a platform equipped with a work bench. At the base of the structure was a full shelf for spares, tools, etc., and four castors were fitted, with no provision for 'jacking feet' or stabilising legs. Extension height could be varied from 7ft to 12ft (2.1 to 3.6m) by the use of extension frames. The type M consisted of two basic type N units, each with a ladder at one end and connected by a metal bridge piece. It was designed with the modern twins in mind – Blenheim, Whitley, Wellington, Hampden, Harrow and Bombay – to give a platform on either side of the engine. No work benches were fitted and the extension range was as the type N. On this platform each of the units had large, car-type mobility wheels and four stabilising jacks designed to lift the platform clear of the ground. Total weight of a type M was 1904lb (864kg) against the 2352lb (1067kg) of a type N unit.

Most of the units described above had to be manhandled, as much of the equipment had no wheels and collecting the necessary items and dragging them

Aircraft Inspection Platform Type C. A general-purpose platform which has had a very long life and is still in use. The platform height is adjustable from 5ft 6in to 8ft (1.7–2.4m). An access ladder is fitted and the chassis has steadying pads and hand-operated clamps.

Aircraft Inspection Platform Type N. A general hangar unit for servicing and access. The bench was provided with storage drawers, an access ladder was provided and the height of the platform could be mechanically adjusted from 7ft to 12ft (2.13–3.65m) by the addition of extension boxes.

An early type, possibly pre-WW2, GP aircraft-servicing platform awaiting disposal at the Aerospace Museum at Cosford, September 1986. This would be a hefty weight to move around. Various trestles and jacks can be seen in the background.

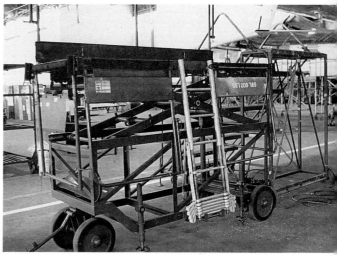

An adjustable Mobile Servicing Platform Mk 2, generally known as the 'Safety Raiser', in use on a VC 10 at RAF Brize Norton in June 1987.

Adjustable Mobile Aircraft Servicing Platform Mk 2. The progenitor of the popular 'Safety Raiser', a general-purpose servicing platform. The platform could be hydraulically adjusted between the heights of 4ft 6in and 9ft 6in (1.37–2.89m) and a telescopic ladder was fitted. The chassis had four jacking feet and was made to be towed. A bridge piece was available to be used between two units.

to the aircraft took up a disproportionate amount of time, which was not always taken into account in the days before Planned Servicing. On the other hand, once in position they saved time.

A somewhat more ambitious version of the types N and M was the 1958 Mk 2 Adjustable Mobile Servicing Platform, otherwise known as the Safety Raiser, a well-known and most useful platform manufactured by Zip-Up. The early models were designed for hangar and dispersal use, but the increasing height of the multi-engined aircraft with excessively high tail units and rear-mounted engines, such as the VC10 and Tristar class, created problems of access for checks and maintenance which these platforms could not solve. The Safety Raiser consisted of a working platform which was extensible, mounted on scissors support frame on a steel-box frame chassis. Elevating and lowering the platform was by hydraulic ram connecting the scissor arms from a hand-operated pump. The platform was very robust and mounted four rubber-

tyred wheels, a steering bogie, four stabilising jacks and had rubber buffers to protect the aircraft. It could, like the type M, be arranged with two units with a metal bridge piece if required, but when used in this configuration the SWL was reduced to 400lb from the 600lb of the single unit. Total weight of the GSE with accessories was 2015lb (914kg).

Mention has been made of the increasing size and weight of bomber and transport aircraft, the under-wing servicing of which could be very awkward. The GSE used on the Sunderland for this type of servicing prior to, and during, WW2 highlighted this problem. A tower ladder platform for reaching the wings and engines of the aircraft when out of the water – in this example – was in the form of a wire-braced four-sided wood construction, very similar to an old-style aircraft fuselage mounted end-on on a four-wheeled base. A small working platform with rails was raised and lowered on this structure by the platform occupant operating a cable-winding gear. The danger was that the operating height plus the weight of the tradesman and his working equipment could produce a critical 'angle of lean'. This particular piece of equipment had previously been used on large biplanes and was really quite unsuited to the more modern types of monoplanes.

In 1959, rather late, a large elevating servicing platform came into use specifically for under-wing servicing and began the specialised 'dock' equipment which entered service for use on V bombers and other large, high aircraft. The platform structures followed the pattern of aircraft manufacturers' assembly platforms, whereby a form of docking was made from scaffolding into which the aircraft was placed for final systems fitting and checking prior to roll out. Their size made them impracticable for use on operational stations, even on some repair MUs, and a modified form, designed still on the dock principle, was introduced to give the necessary access to the complex systems, engines and mainplane interiors. It was lighter in weight and easier to assemble.

The equipment was based generally on a double safety-raiser theme, with two very similar units being bridged by a telescopic central section; both units were adjustable hydraulically by hand-operated pumps. An additional extension of 1ft (30.5cm) could be obtained by the use of extension pillars. All the adjustment aimed to allow for any sloping (dihedral) angle of the underwing. The unit was equipped with a telescopic ladder and the platform chassis was mounted on four solid rubber-tyred castors and fitted with stabilising jacks. Maximum height was 8ft (2.4m) the SWL was 1200lb (544kg) and the unit weighed in at 3920lb (1778kg).

For higher access, as to rudder hinges, tops of fuselages, the Giraffe Servicing Aircraft Ladder type AA Mk2, was more suitable – it had a working height of up to 38ft (11.6m) according to type. It

An early 'Safety Raiser'-type hydraulically adjustable servicing platform in the disposal area of the Aerospace Museum at Cosford in June 1985.

Major servicing of a Sunderland at RAF Pembroke Dock after the war. A tower ladder is in use at left with, between the figures, a GP flat-top ladder type B. Far right is a swing-back ladder designed for servicing in a minimal space. Also shown are a vacuum cleaner (in the foreground) and an early scaffold-type access ladder (behind the vacuum cleaner) *(Flight International)*.

Large Elevating Aircraft Servicing Platform. A platform used in the 1960s for underwing servicing of large aircraft. The platform floor was in three sections, a telescopic centre section being connected to two outer sections mounted on scissor support frames. The height adjustment was hydraulically operated by hand lever-operated pumps, and extension pillars enabled the outer ends of the outer sections to be raised an additional 12in (30.5cm). The chassis was mounted on four castor wheels and fitted with stabilising jacks.

A Giraffe-type hydraulically adjustable servicing platform stored at RAF St Athan. The strengthening plates of the chassis are clearly visible.

became as popular as the Safety Raiser. It was operated by a single, large hydraulic jack connecting the base unit to a jointed framework on a wheeled chassis. Each half of the framework carried steps which, at maximum height, could form a long continuous ladder up to a safety-railed platform. The operation of elevating the platform was controlled by the operator using either a hand or electro-hydraulic pump. Stability was achieved by foot-operated jacks in the base of the chassis. Normal SWL was 600lb (272kg) which reduced to 250lb (113kg) when an accessory jib was fitted to the working platform. As its name implies the Giraffe is tall, slim and far reaching. It weighs 2016lb (914kg).

The Giraffe inspired a variety of designs, but it was the invention of the multi-positional, hydraulically operated, single-boom servicing platform by Simon Engineering that revolutionised this type of access equipment. Originally planned for civilian use with fire-fighting and access to such things as pylons and overhead cables in mind, a model was soon adapted for aircraft use. The ultimate to date is the Simon Topper, originally adapted for use on

the Nimrod and Tornado, but very soon available for many similar-size aircraft and many jobs on, and away from, the airfield. It is hydraulically manipulated to almost every position required, except upside down, from a comprehensively equipped control panel. The machine is towable by MT, handler or by hand. A unique and most useful feature against the heavy-handed operator is that microswitches are fitted on the platform to stop the machine immediately it makes contact with the aircraft or other structure. Although heavy, this particular unit has the advantages of compactness when stored and the boom design, giving safe working facility in a confined space, which is a great bonus with the present trend towards hardened aircraft shelters.

In service at RAF Brize Norton, home of large transport and freighter aircraft, the VC10 and

A Giraffe servicing aircraft ladder type AA Mk 2 in use at
RAF Waddington, 28 April 1990.

A Simon Topper hydraulically operated adjustable
servicing platform displaying its versatility on a Tornado of
RAF Cottesmore (Simon-Gala).

Side view of the Simon Topper hydraulic work platform, a new design to give multi-articulation movement, powered by an electric motor. The canopy is raised to show the motor and the pump. RAF St Athan, May 1986.

Pssst! Want a lift? Assorted Giraffes and servicing platforms in the storage area of 16 MU RAF Stafford for maintenance and refurbishing, 6 July 1993 *(RAF Official ST/450.93)*.

TriStar, noted for their height, is a Telescopic Lift, Model 60HDR, by JLG, which is rather massive in size. It is a double-boom type, each boom having a telescopic arm operated by a chain and carrying a heavy padded enclosed platform containing the controls for operating. The booms are mounted on a large, steel turntable, itself mounted on a massive steel box chassis with one axle fixed and the other steerable. The unit is fitted with a towbar and all four wheels have heavy-duty tyres. Operating height range is 59–95ft (18–29m) and weight is 9.98 tons (10,140kg).

There were other access requirements, such as for refuelling, which developed to keep pace with modern needs. Much of the refuelling during and immediately after WW2 involved the refuelling mechanics getting a leg up on to the wing from the front or rear trailing edge, the scrabbling up the wing slope certainly not doing the wing surface much good. When the jets entered service much care had to be taken to maintain the high-speed gloss finish, of a Meteor for example, by the use of wing mats, so a more positive access to the refuelling points was needed. A refueller's antecedents would soon be questioned if he scratched *that* finish.

Beside their surface finish the jets also had large-capacity fuel tanks. Refuelling was a comparatively slow procedure despite the increase in the gallons per minute rate of the heavy tankers, partly because the refuelling mechanic would slow down as he reached tank-top level. This problem was solved by underwing pressure refuelling, whereby the hose was locked into the tank from below; this allowed a faster fuel flow rate and at the same time also solved the surface damage and access problem. The introduction of hydrant refuelling brought in a piece of GSE to help reach wing tanks on large aircraft from below and is being introduced to a number of stations; it is a stand which carries a platform and two fuel hoses to connect to an aircraft's fuel tanks and which feeds fuel pumped from the buried hydrant fuel tanks via a manifold and filters on the stand. The GSE is towable, has stabilising legs and an access ladder to the operator's platform.

The extreme height of the Beverley, one of the tallest aircraft ever to be in service, presented a problem that has been mentioned in Chapter 2 – that of hangarage for servicing. The natural follow-on from that operation was to gain access to those components which were at altitude, a logical corollary to

Platform side of the Simon Topper, showing the control panel and cable, and how the movement is folded. RAF St Athan, May 1986.

A special stand utilised for underwing pressure refuelling on TriStar aircraft, RAF Brize Norton, June 1987. Note the hydrant hose connecting points (bottom right).

the Sunderland. But progress had been made from the tower ladder, and the firm of Zip-Up had produced a snap-together structure which, in its first use in the RAF, was designated by the quaint name of Hi-Way Fabricated Constructural Equipment. It had what at the time was the unique feature of being assembled by snap-action hooks which eliminated any bolts. With other components this light alloy structure could be used to build a variety of step and span staging.

The original Beverley staging had proved to be rather heavy, presenting a problem overseas, so a much lighter staging was designed to be stowed in dismantled form in the nose doors of the aircraft. The original staging was retained for base deep servicing and did the job well. By the installation of these docks in MUs the pattern was set and the systems continued, and still do, for the very heavy aircraft now comprising almost the entire RAF transport fleet. The structure for the VC10 shows a highly complex scaffolding enveloping the aircraft, particularly the tail unit, to such an extent that one wonders if a specialist engineer was employed for this job. Much the same parameters apply to the TriStar and Hercules.

A JLG telescopic lift model 60HDR in the ground-equipment bay at RAF Brize Norton. It appears to be chain-operated and the platform is protected from damaging aircraft by pressure pads and carries the operating controls and panel. June 1987.

Hi-Way fabricated constructional equipment (Zip-Up), utilised as access platforms on either side of a Tornado being serviced at RAF Cottesmore, June 1987.

Zip-Up tubular steel-fabricated constructional equipment fitted with mobility wheels in storage at RAF St Athan, May 1986. A very old oil-waste trolley is on the right.

Hi-Way structural access lightweight staging in its simpler form, being used for servicing a Lockheed Neptune of the Royal Netherlands Air Force at the Aerospace Museum, Cosford, in September 1986.

The portable staging which could be dismantled and assembled, designed for the Beverley but found to be unsuitable for overseas operations away from firm base airfields. This early 'dock' tended to sink into sand under its own weight. It was afterwards superseded by the Zip-Up staging that could be carried in one of the aircraft's clam doors *(MOD PRB 12901)*.

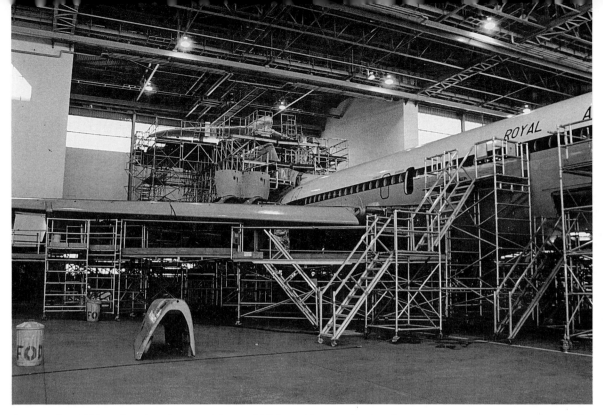

A view of a VC10 undergoing deep servicing at RAF Brize Norton, showing the extensive access structure required for modern large aircraft. The underwing servicing access platform (dock) can be clearly seen. June 1987.

A Vulcan on major Planned Servicing inspection, showing the amount of ground equipment required to service it, and also the first application of the 'dock' system of underwing servicing. January 1973 *(RAF Official 2207/6, Bruce Robertson Collection)*.

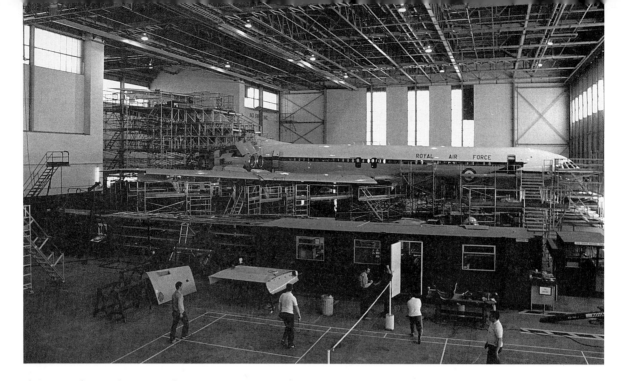

This general view shows a Vickers VC10 at RAF Brize Norton undergoing deep servicing in the 1312ft (400m) long servicing hall. The cabins in the foreground accommodate the servicing staff and records offices. June 1987.

The tail unit of a VC10 almost enveloped in scaffolding which supports access platforms and ladders during deep servicing at RAF Brize Norton, June 1987.

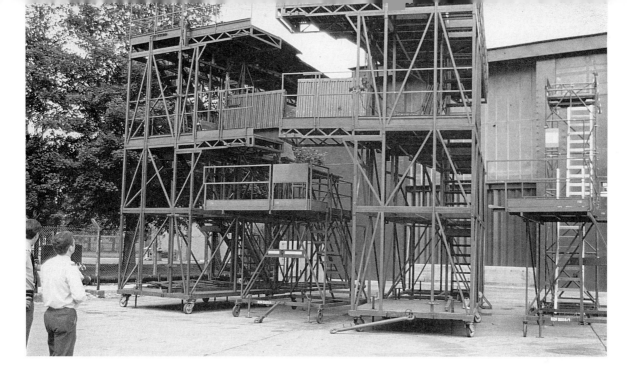

A BS TriStar tail-unit servicing platform complete with mobility towbars held in their bays at RAF Brize Norton in June 1987. F/Lt Barratt, Engineer Officer, looks on.

Side view of TriStar tail-unit access ladders and platforms at RAF Brize Norton in June 1987. A triumph of modern scaffolding, and very light in weight for its size.

It is possible that the only large aircraft that will remain in RAF service in the foreseeable future – spaceships excepted – will be the passenger and freight machines, and that they will operate from stations equipped specifically for their use. For the rest operational aircraft tend to be designed smaller; the Tornado is far more deadly than the Vulcan and consequently, although some of the aerospace (present nomenclature) equipment has to be specialised, it is far easier and more economical to design and produce 'general purpose' GSE which can make the tradesmen's task so much easier and be air transportable.

When operating on the routes of Transport Command, the high access of some aircraft coupled with inadequate GSE available on some airfields into which these aircraft go can tax the ingenuity of the ground trades. An example of this was a Hercules transport which required vital inspection of its fin and rudder hinges – and the consequent removal of a nest! – at RAF Decimommanu in Sardinia with no suitable access equipment available. Chief Technician Powell, the aircraft's crew chief, donned his thinking cap. All that was available was a transport loader type 25KT, also known as a Condec, a large self-propelling vehicle designed to transfer miscellaneous cargo loads up to 25,000lb (1134kg). The vehicle platform, on which was mounted a cab, could be raised, lowered, rolled and pitched by hydraulic power supplied from the prime mover engine and controlled from the cab through flexible cables. A telescopic ladder gave access to the platform and the vehicle could be driven on the

Chief Technician Powell exercises his technical ingenuity and places a Giraffe type AA servicing ladder on to a Transfer Loader type 25KT, known also as a Condec, to service the rudder hinges of a Hercules Transport at RAF Decimommanu in Sardinia . . .

. . . the source of the trouble was a bird's nest! *(C/Tech Powell)*.

road; it was also air transportable. This particular one was owned by the Italian Air Force.

Chief Tech Powell mounted the station Giraffe type AA servicing ladder on to the Condec loading platform with the aid of a fork lift. This particular Condec had a slight hydraulic leak which produced the sag characteristic shown in the photo, which Powell considered quite hairy when operating the combination at extreme height! But it did the job

and illustrates that RAF training, coupled with good thinking and taking a calculated risk, can often produce the result required.

As a result of what may be found on inspections, or faults diagnosed, it may be necessary to lift an aircraft or to remove major sub-assemblies, and for this work special equipment is normally required.

Chapter 5
Lifting

The earliest form of 'equipment' for lifting an aeroplane was a strong pair of arms and, perhaps, a box or plank to support it. The term 'lifting' is used here in a general sense to include the methods that are used to raise an aeroplane, and items associated with it, off the ground for purposes other than salvage. An aircraft has to be lifted many times during its life – for example, during its servicing cycles, a wheel change, the necessary testing of its undercarriage or to have the front guns harmonised. The types of ground equipment used for this operation may fall into two main categories, each performing the same service – trestling, which was used generally up to about 1937, and jacking from that time on – all merely a matter of mechanics. These are the lifts directly concerned with the aircraft. There is a third method of lifting utilising hoists, gantries, cranes, etc., for all the associated parts and equipment, and now even a complete aircraft as illustrated.

This account is of methods employed from 1918, when trestling had become established; from then on, despite advances in aircraft design, trestling remained fundamentally unaltered until 1937–38. The light weight of the early aircraft ensured that their manhandling was correspondingly easier when the time came for the aircraft to be lifted on to wood trestles for repair, dismantling, erection and/or rigging. These were placed, one under the front and rear of a tractor fuselage, or under the engine bearers and tail of a pusher such as the DH2 or FE2B, and one under each wing. That, basically, is how it is still done even if the lifting medium has altered. The method of adjustment when putting the early aircraft into rigging position was usually achieved by packing the fixed-height trestles with tapered wood blocks and using spirit levels in the appropriate places on the aircraft to level the fuselage fore and aft and laterally.

When the importance of correct rigging to aerodynamic performance was generally realised during WW1, attempts were made to make the trestles more accurate and provide them with a degree of adjustment. In the 1920s trestles became cross-braced for strength and some were custom-built to a designed height – for the tail unit, for example – others to accept a rod which was passed through positioning holes in the rear fuselage, which was then lifted and the rod placed on the trestle to give an approximate rigging position. A universal, or general purpose, trestle introduced in the 1920s and used to support the rear fuselage was of the adjustable-tripod type of all-metal construction and consisted of three legs connected at the top by a sheet steel plate through which passed centrally, and vertically, a screwed ram further braced by a second plate in the form of a steel tray about halfway down the legs. At the top of the ram was fitted an ash-bearer bar and movement up and down was by a three-spoke capstan. Operating range was 3ft 8in to 5ft (1–1.5m) and the trestle could carry up to 500lb (227kg) loads.

Early type wood trestles made locally for both nose and tail, being used to support a bent Sopwith Pup during salvage in 1917. The 6 on the fuselage could indicate the aircraft's unit.

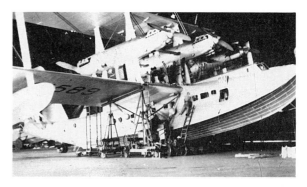

Special tail-wing trestles are combined to form a gantry (and mobile) in use on a Short Sarafan during maintenance. Lack of ground equipment is noticeable. (in 1932)

A Vickers Wellington Mk 10 being prepared for the Bomber Command section of the RAF Hendon Museum in December 1983. The picture also shows a wing gantry which was used to assemble a Vickers Vimy, a hydraulic jack and a bomb trolley.

Mainplane Steady Trestle. Height-adjustable steady trestle, used in pairs to provide support under the mainplanes of large aircraft. A padded light alloy beam is mounted at the top of the ram, and the tubular steel trestle is made mobile by two wheels and a towbar. The legs can be extended by three one-foot (30cm) stages and the ram extended by a hand wheel on a threaded shaft. A step and six rungs are welded to one leg for access.

Depending on size later trestles gave a loading range from 650 to 4480lb (295kg–2 tonnes).

The first versions of these were introduced into the RAF in 1931 with a plain ash-bearer bar and fitted with quick-operating cranks to the jacking head operating lever. They were designed for all parts of the trestle to be quickly interchangeable, with ten different sets of sizes to give height variety from 2ft 3in to 6ft 3in (0.69–1.9m). Steadying trestles with padded bars were placed under the bottom wing main spar or suitably strengthened ribs.

A form of trestling which developed from the rather primitive method of using double large stepladders and planks which were sometimes used for large biplane upper-wing change support was a special gantry which consisted of two vertical pillars with strong bases, connected by an adjustable padded horizontal support bar, forming in effect a

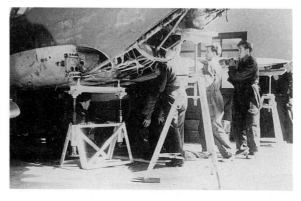

A tripod-steadying trestle under the nose and port wing, with a general-purpose trestle under the fuselage help to raise this Spitfire for assembly for an exhibition *(R. Milner)*.

A three-ton Colossus mobile gantry on servicing at RAF Stafford in July 1986.

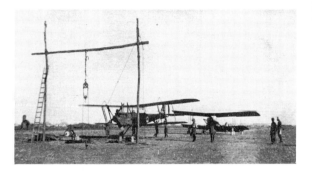

Engine change of an RE8 at Amara in Mesopotamia in March 1917, using what must surely have been one of the first (though improvised) gantries.

A GP trestle from between the wars with two of its side stays missing. All the sizes of stays were interchangeable to make up a variety of sizes of trestles. Aerospace Museum, Cosford, February 1988.

A typical pre-Planned Servicing scene, prior to the introduction of that scheme with its attendant order and equipment designed specifically for faster turn-round of inspection times. This photo shows typical jacking for a Hawker Hunter; the boxes are the tradesmen's toolboxes, which were to be discontinued under the new scheme. RAF Leuchars, June 1955 (Bruce Robertson collection).

high trestle. One vertical pillar was placed near the leading edge of the upper wing near the tip, and the other at the opposite trailing edge. The support bar was then passed under the plane bottom surface and attached to the vertical pillars by pins through the nearest appropriate holes in the pillars that allowed the weight of the wing to be taken just on the support bar. Heavy-top mainplanes of the large biplanes, such as Vickers Vimy and DH10, required another gantry placed inboard near the wing attachment point; in some cases provision was made to fit spreader-bar cables to the wings for lifting by crane.

Most aircraft, especially those with long wingspans, presented a problem of stability when jacked up, particularly if work had to be done on the outboard mainplanes. To give that necessary solidity special tripod telescopic trestles, a modified version of the universal type, were brought into use in pairs. The tubular steel structures had a working variation in height from 8ft 6in to 15ft (2.6–4.6m) achieved in three 1ft (30.5cm) stages to 11ft 6in (3.5m), the remaining 3ft 6in (1.07m) extension being achieved by a central ram assembly controlled

A range of typical older type hydraulic jacks at Newark (Wimbourne) Museum. The three larger jacks are 25-ton versions, and a Colossus one-ton gantry can be seen to the left, together with a fire truck. At the rear is a 'Queen Mary' low-loader aircraft-salvage trailer. July 1983.

by a handwheel fitted with a threaded shaft. The trestles had a light alloy beam fitted with two suitably padded supports and were equipped with transportation wheels and a retractable towbar; the beam could be removed and stowed on the trestle. A useful point, six rungs and a step were welded to one leg to aid access to the trestle top. The trestle weighed 504lb (229kg).

Trestle design kept pace with the first of the Expansion aircraft of 1934, but the increase in aircraft weight led to designs that might lead one to suppose that the designer had served his apprenticeship on the old Forth Bridge. One such specific to the Whitley, for example, needed a minimum of two strong airmen to move it over a smooth hangar floor, and to take it out on the airfield – for de-bogging an aircraft, for instance – four or five airmen could be struggling with this hernia-provoking item. As aircraft became heavier, so a more compact and efficient means of lifting was required.

The final stage of trestle development, just prior to the introduction of the hydraulic jack, was the all-metal universal jacking trestle. This was made from angle-iron in various sizes and incorporated two lifting jacking heads operated by handwheels and ratchet levers. The trestles could accept metal rails and stays of different sizes, with an ash crossbar, some bars shaped as formers to fit under the contour of the rear fuselage. The bars were superseded on some trestles by small pillars into which a bar, placed through the fuselage, could fit. The UV trestles were the ultimate general issue; they stayed in service for many years and are still in isolated use for such aircraft as the Spitfire and others of that size, for example, on the Battle of Britain Flight.

A 25-ton four-legged hydraulic jack, fitted with mobility wheels and showing the stability plates and hydraulic jack layout, after servicing at RAF St Athan in May 1986.

The principle of the hydraulic jack was not new – it was merely awaiting the development of suitable stronger and lighter materials to enable it to be used on aircraft. It was preceded by the first mechanically operated tripod jacks, direct descendents of the tripod trestle described on page 71, which were mechanically operated by lever-ratchet screwed rams, fitted with lifting collars. The ratchet was two-way for up and down operation and these jacks were most effective. The first hydraulic jacks operated on similar principles but utilising hydraulic pressure. They were normally fitted with three (later, four) legs braced to the central body, with adjustable 'floating' pads to even out inequalities of floor level. Early hydraulic jacks were operated by a lever which raised a screwed ram; on reaching the required height the ram was locked by a screwed steel collar. When the ram was required to be lowered, sufficient pressure was pumped by the lever to ease the collar from its seat and the collar screwed clear, when a small release valve lever on the jack body was operated to release the hydraulic pressure slowly; the weight of the aircraft did the rest.

A 33.6-tonne four-legged two-stage hydraulic jack, used on such aircraft as the Nimrod, being serviced at RAF St Athan in May 1986.

A Zwicky SkiHi model S2528 28-tonne main jack shown in use on a VC10 at RAF Brize Norton under the forward fuselage. The jack has air and oil control and has a three-stage extension to 13ft 3½in (4.04m). June 1987.

The oil cylinder with its pump-operating lever was either incorporated in the base of the central body or attached and interconnected to the cylinder/central body. When used to lift an aircraft a special pad, peculiar to the type of aircraft and made by the manufacturer, was fitted on the ram head to engage with a socket concealed usually behind a plate on the under fuselage and/or underwing. This method is still in use today and all aircraft are specially strengthened in their design and construction to spread the stress points of this single-point jacking, as it is known, a method whereby one only hydraulic jack is used under each side of the centre section, or near each inboard engine in the case of multi-engined aircraft, and one under the tail.

Hydraulic jack development has been continuous, mainly in performance, and it arrived on the scene in time to perform sterling service during WW2 – and so ease the aircraft tradesmen's job somewhat. A good example of a GP type jack is the 5-ton four-legged Hydraulic Lifting Jack type G of 1948. The jack came in three marks according to weight lift: Mk 1 160lb (73kg), Mk 2 214lb (98kg), Mk 3 270lb

(122kg) and a lift range which varied from 1ft 10in to 3ft (56–91cm) according to mark. The jack was of the double-ram type operated by a single acting force pump fitted to the side of the body. The unit could also be used as a bipod and both vertical and arc lifts could be taken. Later jacks are fully mobile, have either one or more legs adjustable or telescopic, and can raise greater weights for disproportionately less weight of their own. The latest Zwicky SkyHi 25-ton main jacks also use air as a means of helping fluid flow in the ram, a practical application of the new technical 'in' word 'pneudraulics'.

The many uses to which a hydraulic jack could be put made the work rate of airmen much easier at a time when aircraft weight – and their components – was rising rapidly. One of these uses was in wheel changing, just when the increased flying, particularly in training schools, was having a detrimental effect on tyre wear. This most useful jack, which was very heavy, had the jack ram, lifting assembly and operating lever mounted on a steel vee chassis, the whole fitted with two fixed and two castoring wheels. Additionally, two car-type pneumatic

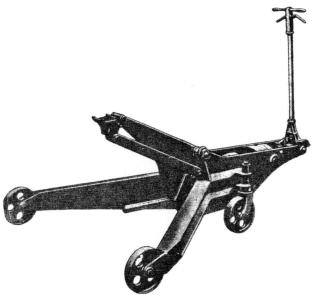

Lifting Hydraulic Jack 3½ Tons. A type of jack established for very many years, used primarily for wheel changing. The jack is mounted on four wheels and comprises a hydraulic ram and lifting assembly.

A tripod hydraulic jack, ex-BA, showing the hydraulic reservoir which can be fed with pressure air. This is used for the initial movement of the jack until the full load of the aircraft starts to be taken, when the operator reverts to hand pumping. The transportation wheels are raised and lowered by their own hydraulic jacks, as in the example shown on the right. Aerospace Museum, Cosford, September 1986.

SkiHi Hydraulic Wheel-changing Lifting Jack 3½ Tons. A developed version of the previous 3½-ton jack, this type is designed for raising the bogie and changing wheels on VC10 aircraft. It incorporates independent high- and low-pressure manually operated pumps to vary load lifting. The jack body is box-sectioned, horizontally mounted on three sprung wheels and has a positioning handle.

wheels could be fitted to the chassis for transport and, if the jack had to be used on soft ground, as it frequently was, two flanged runways were provided. The type A had an 8-ton (8.13 tonne) lift of 4ft 6in (1.4m) from a closed height of 10in (25.4cm). In its original form it was issued in the RAF as a Jack, High Lifting, in 1923 and has remained virtually unaltered since.

A late development of the lever jack was the 35 ton (35.56 tonne) SkyHi model S3501 designed to lift the bogie of a Vickers VC10 for wheel changing. This jack comprised a horizontal, square-box section steel body mounted on three sprung wheels, which carried the hydraulic telescopic ram, a high-

An 8-ton salvage trolley-type mechanical jack type A, with detachable mobile wheels, held in stock at RAF Stafford in July 1986. An obsolete item that did a fine job of work in its day, although it was far too heavy. It was a developed version of the 3½ ton.

When sheer legs are not available, look for the nearest tree! Carrying out an engine change on a Voisin LAS of 7 (Naval) Squadron at Koanda Iringi, German East Africa, in 1916, using basics (J.M. Bruce/S. Leslie Collection).

Engine change on a Short 184 of the RNAS, showing one of the prime uses for sheer legs. This is an early type B (J.M. Bruce/S. Leslie Collection).

(38cm) and an air pump for use in low temperatures which, by applying pressure in the fluid chamber, assisted the fluid flow. Safety split sleeves for locking the ram when under load were supplied. Weight of the jack was 100lb (45.4kg).

The mother of invention spawned an innovative brood when it came to devising methods of lifting in conditions of extreme austerity. One such was to use a local tree branch or its trunk with others to form a makeshift gantry on which to span the job and secure a primitive rope tackle. If the countryside was blessed with trees and a pulley hoist was available, a tree might be modified to act as a single sheer leg, which was one of the earliest forms of lifting, dating back through the misty curtains of time and which found a place in most armies; it entered the RAF via the Royal Engineers and RFC. This extremely useful piece of ground equipment was in constant use for aircraft salvage, changing engines and lifting

pressure pump for use up to the 35 tons (35.56 tonnes) and a low-pressure pump to give a quick lift for light loads, each pump manually operated independently by a (stowable) handle. The jack weight was 260lb (118kg). Maximum ram lift was 11in (28cm), with a further 6in (15cm) with a ram extension fitted.

Single pillar jacks – sophisticated versions of car jacks – were employed for general use. An example was the 15 ton (15.24 tonne) pillar jack for aircraft. This had a triple ram which gave a lift of 1ft 3in

Sheer legs type A being used to raise a very bent RE8 until support trestles can be secured under the fuselage. Early post-WW1 *(Bruce Robertson Collection).*

the light fuselages of the early biplanes. Sheer legs first comprised two long logs lashed together to form an inverted vee and braced by ropes from the apex to a picket screwed into the ground, or the nearest strong point, at the bottom rear. They usually carried a rope or wire cable over the apex from which the main lifting tackle hung. Subsequent development included a chain instead of a cable, wound by a hand-operated ratchet drum designed to prevent the lifted load overcoming the winding gear, a third leg in place of the bracing cable and carrying the ratchet drum, the whole on a triangular wood base complete with castors to which the three carpentered legs were fitted. The base was designed to carry counterweights to offset the heavier loads. The RAF sheer legs proved their worth in overseas areas where stations tended to be isolated and modern lifting equipment (for the day) was not readily available. Before WW2 all RAF stations had on charge a force-landing kit which included sheer legs and was kept for use by station workshops.

By the beginning of WW2 the two main sheer legs in the RAF were the types A and B. Type A was a three-legged wooden structure, suitably reinforced at connecting points by metal plates, and capable of vertically lifting 2.5 tonnes to a maximum height of 21ft 6in (7m). The legs were attached to, and braced by, a triangular wooden base which had a roller fitted at each corner point for mobility only. The whole could easily be dismantled and was normally stored in this condition. Weight was 896lb (407kg). Type B in its original form was much lighter, in the traditional two-legged inverted vee with extensive use of wire cables for stabilising, bracing and anchoring. It was modified to be airportable. When in use the type B, by virtue of its

Type B sheer legs being used to lift a Fairy Gordon of 35 Squadron on to a barge at Port Sudan in October 1935 *(R. Lee).*

construction, was required to tilt forward over the item to be lifted – it was liable to collapse if tilted to the rear, owing to the absence of any forward support. This weakness was corrected in later versions. The earlier type had a lifting capacity of 1000lb (454kg) to a height of 17ft 6in (5.3m), but was subsequently modified to a welded tubular steel framework fixed construction when, with the aid of a hand-operated winch and steel cable, it could lift a maximum of 2 tons (2.03 tonnes). The lift was a revision of the earlier type B in that its C of G was within the centre of the vee base, which gave greater stability. The unit was fitted with two fixed and one steerable rubber-tyred castor wheels.

The concept of the gantry was as old as the sheer legs and even in its most primitive form of two vertical tree trunks surmounted by a horizontal trunk it proved very useful to the RFC squadrons forced to use it on active service for changing engines. Sufficiently supported, these gantries did a great job and it was only natural that properly designed and engineered gantries should make their appearance on the inventories of squadrons and workshops. Gantries of 20-ton (20.32 tonne) capacity with spans of 40ft (12.2m) plus are now in use, mainly at MUs and for some aspects of salvaging.

Although sheer legs are available on the established stations they tended, as time passed, to be superseded by small mobile hoists and cranes – naturally enough, as any RAF tradesman would prefer these more compact units. The early hoists, cranes and gantries followed a similar principle in that they were all hand-operated winches with cables running over pulleys. With later modifications winches were extensively used. With all lifting gear after WW2 new regulations enforced the safety factor and all such GSE have to display their safe working load (SWL).

The hoist principle was adapted quite cleverly in some areas, as in pre-war RAF Peshawar station workshops on the North-West Frontier of India, as it then was. A tubular steel framework was built on to a Crossley chassis in the form of a braced structure running fore and aft, along the top of which was fixed a steel runway for a double-pulley hoist. The runway overhung the rear of the vehicle sufficiently to give clearance for the removal of engines from Audax and similar aircraft. It was put to good use.

In the years immediately following WW2 the tradesmen had an adequate number of suitable

A Crossley recovery vehicle modified to carry a vertical hoist on a transverse track and used to lift a pranged Audax of 20 Squadron for transport back to base at RAF Peshawar in 1937 (J.P. Murray).

hoists and cranes for the aircraft then in service, which included several 'heavies'. When Transport Command began to operate increasingly heavy transports such as Beverley and Britannia, and Bomber Command received its V types, the lifting equipment was still more than adequate, but the hoists were developed further in strength, capacity and versatility. The multi-purpose servicing hoist is

A selection of slings for all purposes at RAF Cosford servicing squadron in July 1986.

A portable 20cwt (1016kg) jib crane in store at RAF St Athan in May 1986. Of early vintage, it is used by the Technical Training School.

An MT jack crane, used for vehicle-engine removal, on servicing at RAF St Athan in May 1986.

an example. This single-pillar hoist mounted on a tee-shaped base had a variety of functions, for with suitable attachments it could vary its SWL. It could also become a fork lift with a range of heights from 1½in to 7ft (38mm–2.13m) and as a servicing platform it had a flat surface 3 x 2ft (90 x 60cm) and a SWL of 560lb (254kg). The floor height could be adjusted from 5ft 10in to 13ft (1.78–4m). A variety of curved jibs, which ran up and down a track in the pillar, gave a range of 224 to 1344lb (102–610kg) SWL and the jib chain hanging length could be adjusted up to 3ft 2in (97cm). To complete the description of this unique hoist it was also designed for use with missiles. Weight is 1550lb (704kg). A

number of these early hoists are still in service – for example at RAF Valley on the BA Hawk in 1993.

Another development is the general purpose engine hoist type B, most successful and of tubular construction with two lattice-type base legs in vee configuration, both braced by tubular members, each with a fixed wheel. At the apex of the base is a hand-operated geared cable drum and a steerable castor wheel. The lifting cable leads up and over an extended fixed jib to the hook. Several variations saw service. One, extensively used at RAF St Athan Technical Training School, is a massively built type, made from channel section girders and incorporating a hand-operated chain drum, its base is ⊓ in

A Mk 1 multi-purpose hoist of the late 1960s, still in use on
a Jet Provost servicing at RAF Finningley in February 1984.

XX171 Hawk under maintenance on the Station Servicing Flight at RAF Valley, 24 September 1992 using the same type
of multi hoist as above. Also shown here are the tail trestle, a set of steps and a servicing platform.

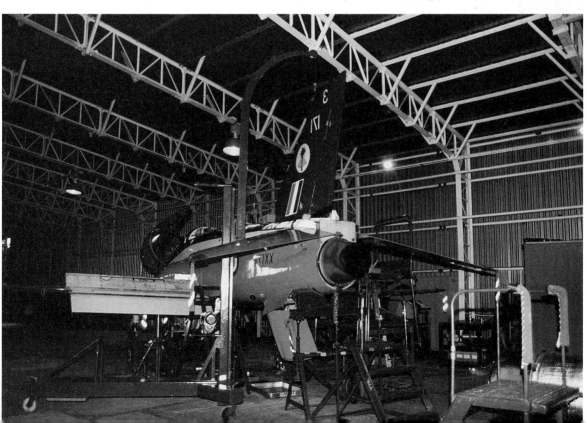

A steam-driven crane of a navy aircraft carrier of WW1 lifts a Short seaplane over the side for launching (MOD).

A general-purpose engine hoist type B in the disposal area at the Aerospace Museum, Cosford, in June 1985, awaiting a posting. One of the most successful for its type, the construction was of tubular steel in a lattice design.

plan form and is fitted with four stabilising screw jacks. The hoist and steerable castor wheel are positioned as type B above and the chain fed to a similar extended jib. Although mainly used by trainee engine trades to lift Derwent engines out of a training Meteor airframe during the 1970s, its lift was restricted by its construction – for example, it was unable to lift such heavy engines as the Hercules.

Also at RAF St Athan was a hoist comprising an open girder-type pillar mounted on a narrow vee base of channel construction. The cable hoist and manually operated gear was mounted at the base of the pillar, the cables running within the open girder to raise and lower a tubular constructed jib and the hook. This section of the hoist was supported on two castor wheels with a fixed wheel at the end of each

A dockside crane in use in the launching of a Short Rangoon after servicing at RAF Gibraltar in 1934 (H. Kevin/Adkin).

leg. Yet another variant on the same theme was to be seen at RAF Finningley, different in layout but on the same principle. This comprised a steel-fabricated base, in the form of a Y with short arms, at the junction of which was a tall, single square pillar channelled to accommodate an adjustable curved jib. The operating cable and gear was

A Coles Hydra Speedcrane with telescopic arm in use at RAF St Athan in May 1986.

An early (1920s) Ransome and Marles crane with solid rubber tyres, lifting a Bristol Pegasus engine out of a Wellesley of B Flight 35 Squadron at RAF Worthy Down in 1938. Sgt Stewart, engine fitter of B Flight, supervises. Note the fine wood trussing between the bays of the hangar roof (MOD H385).

A Coles telescopic crane of very high lifting capacity – probably 100 tons – showing its versatility with a F104 Phantom. Note the wide base of the crane and the arrangement of the support legs *(Coles Ltd)*.

mounted at the base of the pillar. All three arms had a castor wheel.

The first of the self-driven mobile cranes were rather primitive but quite effective, Coles making their first in 1922 on a Tillings-Steven petrol electric bus chassis. It was not used in the UK. Ransome and Marles, another crane firm, built a mobile version in the 1920s, which proved a breakthrough and was still in use in the RAF in 1937, as the photo of a Wellesley engine change at RAF Worthy Down shows. The introduction of the 2-ton (2.03 tonne)

EMA Coles crane, mounted on four or six wheels, was another breakthrough in this field with a very versatile crane that saw RAF service throughout the world. EMA stood for Electric Mobile Aerodrome, as designated in the Air Ministry specification, and the crane came into service in 1938 to be used under Marks 1 to 7. It became an essential part of the salvage teams' equipment, along with the Queen Mary trailers. It was heavy and slow and needed a skilled operator, normally a trained MT driver, to operate, but it was a superb crane and with associated equipment, such as spreader bars, could tackle any number of jobs within its capability. The Coles influence continued with their latest product, the Hydra Group with telescopic booms hydraulically operated.

Chapter 6

Replenishing

The aeroplane today has reached a state of complexity that seems out of all proportion to its original concept. As such it requires correspondingly accurate servicing, which does not imply that it is more prone to system failure, for the aeroplane is actually a very rugged piece of machinery. The

Refuelling a 208 Squadron Armstrong Whitworth Atlas from 4-gallon (18-litre) cans in southern Arabia in winter. Note the message pick-up hook under the fuselage, indicating that this is an Army Co-op squadron aircraft *(MOD print H871).*

military types are more complex than most of their civilian counterparts – Concord excepted – in that they incorporate more purely military systems designed for war. Preparing and servicing all of the great variety of systems require ground support equipment that is becoming more and more universal now, rather than specialised, particularly when applied to the replenishment of fuels, oils, air, oxygen, electrical energy and the checking and testing of highly mechanised and electronically activated operational systems. But specialist equipment is still needed for the sophisticated types and is the

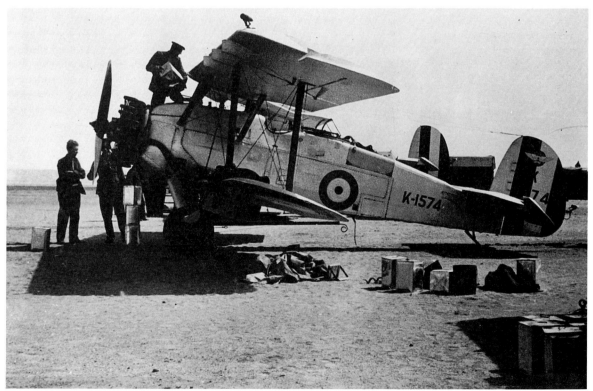

progressively higher price paid for a performance in peace and war that is both the blessing and the curse of modern aviation. By contrast . . .

Swaying under the ground effect of the heated air eddies arising from the hot sands of the landing ground, the Atlas came into land, taxied with its comet tail of dust sucking in a fitter and rigger to the wingtips to help manoeuvre to the open brush shelter, where the pilot switched off the engine. The last sortie of the day and the ground crew began their equivalent of the cavalry's bedding down. Out on the exposed plains of Iraq in 1931, away from base, the procedure, whilst thorough in execution was primitive in content (by today's standards) and refuelling was by hand. There were no fuel bowsers, so the operation necessitated handing up about thirty 4-gallon (18 litre) cans of petrol from the dump to an airman standing in the front cockpit, itself quite a lift; he then reached forward to empty each can into a chamois leather-filtered funnel inserted into the fuselage tank. An exhausting procedure in midsummer temperatures of 120°F (49°C) plus.

Back at base, part of the hard work of that particular chore was alleviated by using the 50-gallon (228-litre) drum type refueller in general use over-

seas. This was a drum fitted with a hand-operated rotary pump mounted on an iron-wheeled trolley, from which the fuel was pumped through a single hose with a nozzle. As the fuel required was often more than the drum's capacity an airman stood by, emptying full cans into the drum as it emptied. Oil was pumped from a very similar piece of equipment which remained virtually unaltered until long after WW2.

The early military aeroplane was very much basic in its needs, requiring fuel, oil and grease and air for the tyres. In 1918 fuel and oil would be supplied from 2 or 4 gallon (9 or 18 litre) cans, although the new fuel bowser was beginning to be seen on the aerodromes. The only other relevant GSE, apart from ladders and trestles, might be a double-cylinder rotary-action air pump for the tyres. The rapid technological advances of WW1, such a feature of that war, heeded the need to get fighter aircraft on to the patrol sector quickly, and the increasing demands of large aircraft with large-capacity fuel tanks. By answering these demands in providing quicker refuelling, the first fuel bowsers made their appearance in 1916 and comprised a similar type of 50-gallon (228-litre) drum to that described above, mounted on its end in a two-wheeled chassis, with the same pumping arrangement.

These were used in all theatres of war and were only efficient so long as the pump seals held, but

A Handley Page 0/100 of 214 Squadron being refuelled from a primitive fuel bowser of about 50-gallons (228-litres) capacity. The fuel is pumped by a hand rotary pump mounted on the drum top. 1 January 1918 *(Bruce Robertson Collection).*

Refuelling an Avro 504J in 1917 with one of the earliest hand-operated rotary-pump refuellers. Note its iron wheels and 'wheelbarrow' handles.

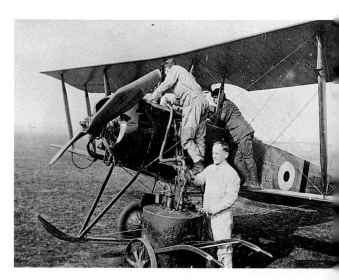

Another 'out in the blue' refuelling of a Vickers Valencia, possibly of 70 Squadron based on RAF Hinaidi, as noted on the petrol barrow. The tins are brought from the dump on the barrow and emptied into the tanks via a chamois-leather filtered funnel *(Murray/Adkin).*

Refuelling a Bristol Blenheim Mk 1. Judging from the primitive camouflage and erks carrying gas masks, this may have been in France or during a UK exercise. 230 octane fuel was introduced in late 1938. The tanker appears to be a Morris Commercial 500-gallon (2280-litre) two-boom of pre-war vintage *(RAF Museum H009 S190).*

were infinitely preferable to lugging tins of petrol up long ladders. Refuelling by hand pumps, although quickly devised, was not entirely successful until petrol-proof seals had been developed. Prior to these the seals would disintegrate under the action of the petrol and small pieces would find their way into engine carburettors with dire results. The 50-gallon (228-litre) drum-type refuellers were used extensively by service and civilian alike; one airline developed a double-drum type in an effort to cope with increased fuel demands from larger fuel tanks. On another aerodrome light rails were laid near the flight line and aircraft were refuelled by a bowser mounted on flanged wheels, which moved along the front of the aircraft. There was a continuing demand for a very much larger capacity and a faster pumping refueller.

As with most aspects of aircraft ground equipment the refuelling of aircraft followed a logical development and the first real prototype of the eventual refueller was designed. This was the Leyland Subsidiary type A fuel truck of the 1920s, which became an interim type as development swung along another path, the fuel bowser trailer idea. Both ideas had their advocates. The latter, with a capacity of up to 450 gallons (2050 litres) was mounted on a four-wheel trailer chassis, had a single hose and was fitted with a mechanical pump driven by a single-cylinder Lister petrol engine housed in a separate compartment for obvious safety reasons.

These Lister engines were hand started via a handled flywheel and were rather cantankerous, but magnificent, and thrived on any petrol available, even on strictly forbidden 100 octane. They were usually towed by tractor, but before the beginning of the Expansion period it had been but a logical progression to join the two paths of bowser development and fit the trailer to a lorry chassis, as in the early Leyland. Another example was that by Bedford, who had developed their type OT mobile bowser in parallel with the trailer bowser. The refueller became completely mobile.

At first only one hose was fitted, but a second was quickly installed and progress remained at this stage, except for the fighter squadron use, where scramble tactics and interceptor theories included rapid refuelling of a large number of fighters at the same time, which produced the Albion 350-gallon (1590-litre) refueller, with its three delivery booms. This came into service in the early 1930s and stayed until after WW2, but the introduction of dispersal tactics as a result of the Battle of Britain negated the three-boom theory.

A variant of the early drum-type 50-gallon (228-litre) refueller was developed for AOP squadron use towards the end of the war and was still employed up to 1957 on advanced landing strips, or towed around the country by the section Land-rover. Such was its success that delivery rate was increased to give a more efficient operation by

Wellesley K7736 of 35 Squadron, the author's aircraft, being refuelled from a 450-gallon (2050-litre) trailer bowser at RAF Worthy Down by the author and friends in 1938 *(MOD print H387)*.

the use of the Lightweight Portable Rellumit type AS2 fuel hand pump, which was capable of delivering about 8 gallons (36 litres) per minute of all grades of aircraft and MT petrol and, later, gas turbine fuel. The fuel was drawn from the drum through a standpipe to the quadruple-acting semi-rotary pump mounted on the standpipe top and thence through a 5 micron filter and 20ft (6m)-long hose and trigger nozzle.

On a number of the older stations in the UK fuel tanks were buried under the tarmac in much the same way as in a normal garage, and aircraft were required to taxi to the point, where steel covers were opened, a hose uncoiled and fuel pumped by an electrically powered pump. Some dangerous congestion occasionally took place when a number of aircraft landed together and all taxied to the point, where there ensued controlled chaos with a positive danger of collision or risk from whirling props (the author saw one non-braked Gordon stop just an inch from the lip of the open covers and was, himself, within a few inches of a revolving prop tip). This system was in use at such RAF stations as Bircham Newton and Worthy Down until 1938, when the threat of war decreed that this slow pre-war style of refuelling was totally unsuited to operational requirements and these installations were discontinued. The method was revised in the 1980s by hydrant refuelling, which is the same pre-war method with the difference that individual tanks are buried under selected dispersal pans and fuel pumped from a main tank via this dispersal tank to the aircraft through two hoses. The

high rate of delivery from the modern hydrant system allies itself well to pressure refuelling; to assist in the task a refuelling and servicing GSE was introduced and is described in Chapter 4.

The probable reason for the introduction of hydrant refuelling was that the parking trend was veering away from the cluster of line/apron parking to semi-dispersal, which meant that several large refuellers would be required to attend to the dispersed aircraft, and on occasions of heavy refuelling needs the tankers themselves might need to be replenished from their main fuel dump. Not altogether expedient and, of course, these very large tankers also present legitimate targets.

Buried fuel installation, or hydrant, at RAF Bircham Newton. Airmen are kneeling by the open cockpit to get at the hose for refuelling. The aircraft is a Fairey 3F. Note the steel-studded boots, ideal for refuelling! About 1932 *(K. Marshall)*.

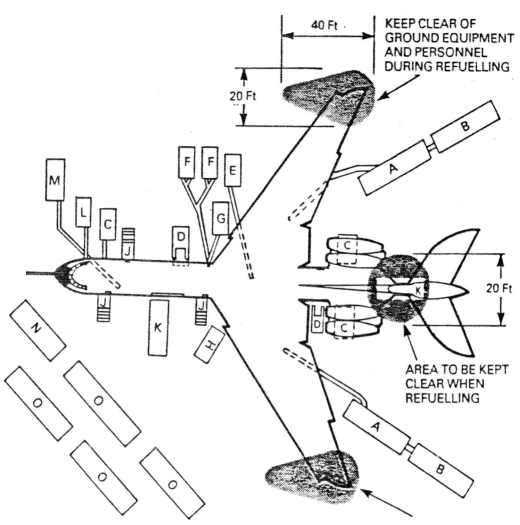

40 Ft

20 Ft

KEEP CLEAR OF
GROUND EQUIPMENT
AND PERSONNEL
DURING REFUELLING

20 Ft

AREA TO BE KEPT
CLEAR WHEN
REFUELLING

KEEP CLEAR OF
GROUND EQUIPMENT
AND PERSONNEL
DURING REFUELLING

A	HIGH CAPACITY REFUELLER
B	REFUELLING TRAILER
C	TOILET TROLLEY
D	FORK LIFT
E	L.P. START TRUCK
F	AIR CONDITIONER
G	WATER BOWSER
H	CATERING TRUCK
J	STEPS
K	SCISSORS TYPE FREIGHT TRUCK
L	OXYGEN
M	ELECTRICAL POWER
N	CREW COACH
O	COACH

TURN ROUND SERVICING
VEHICLE POSITIONING
AND REFUELLING
DANGERS AREAS

Organised chaos, a normal sight as 8 Squadron DH Vampires are replenished at RAF Khormaksar, Aden, in about 1960. In the centre a Land-rover tows an oxygen trolley and at left is a 450-gallon (2050-litre) refueller, possibly for the Mk XIX Anson. Drums of Avtur jet-engine fuel litter the tarmac *(RAF Official)*.

Twin-boom refuellers in use on Vampire aircraft at RAF Oakington, with oxygen trolleys standing by. June 1957.

After the Falklands campaign, RAF Stanley was considerably enlarged, with a new runway capable of accepting the largest aircraft, including TriStar tankers. For these aircraft, specially developed Gloster Saro Mk 10 Javelin foam tenders were based both on Ascension Island – the halfway mark between Britain and the Falklands – and at Stanley in 1985 (Q. & C. Eaton/Adkin).

A 1000-gallon (4546-litre) tanker refueller mounted on a Bedford chassis is test driven over rough ground (Publicity 128890).

A Handley Page Hastings C1 staging through RAF Fayid is given the treatment. The photo shows the ground equipment – and the number of men – required for a mere refuelling stop *(Noble)*.

3000-gallon (13,680-litre) aircraft refueller, or truck, fuel-servicing aircraft 10 ton 6 x 4 D/P mounted on an AEC Mammoth Major TG6RB chassis. This refueller was also adapted to take a snow-plough for runway clearing. RAF Valley, 24 September 1992.

British Aerospace Hunter (with civilian markings G-HUNT) being refuelled at Woodford from a twin-boom tanker, June 1985.

Progress in refuelling throughout WW2 resulted in increased capacity and faster pumping. Fuel tankers reached over 2000-gallon (9120-litre) capacity, which was delivered at up to 200 gallons (912 litres) per minute through double hoses. Some models reverted to the three-directional booms developed for use on the four-engined heavies. A further need for increased pumping rate and capacity was foreseen when the jet aircraft entered service, for these aircraft, or engines, were phenomenally thirsty in their first years of operation, but this high rate of fuel consumption was eased by natural development of the engine and building in larger tanks; and a dramatic increase in refueller

tank capacity, going up to 4000 gallons (18240 litres) with correspondingly faster rate of delivery. Nevertheless, despite its great advantages, the reaction turbine still has a high rate of consumption. Another answer to rapid refuelling needs is a high-pressure refuelling system of the underwing type built into later aircraft and the successful development of air-to-air refuelling for service aircraft.

The first oil replenisher was, of course, a can, but as soon as the 50-gallon (228-litre) hand-pump fuel bowser was introduced in 1917, its possibilities as an oil bowser were quickly evaluated. One of them was converted to pump oil instead of petrol and proved to be so successful in this basic form that it remained in service, suitably modified, up to the advent of the gas turbine.

In its first form it was very similar to the early fuel bowser, with the drum placed vertically on its chassis and modified to pass the thicker oil by a lever-operated hand pump mounted on the drum. In its second and final form it was modified by having a custom-built 45-gallon (205-litre) drum laid on its side in the chassis and incorporating an integral chamber under the drum to accommodate a heater for warming up the oil on freezing days. The first heater was actually a tray on which were placed live coals from, usually, the crewroom coke stove. In some cases the stove was kept burning in cold weather to ensure that the oil did not thicken (or the crewroom occupants freeze!). The bowser had a hand-operated lever pump mounted centrally on top

A 40-gallon (182-litre) pre-WW2 oil bowser, hand-operated by a lever rotary pump. The flap at the base covers a heating housing for warming oil under very cold conditions. In store at RAF St Athan, May 1986.

A 1920s or possibly WW1 oil bowser servicing a Hawker Fury of 17 Squadron. This type of bowser was also adapted for oil draining, as appears in this case. Note the iron wheels and the tradesmen's new issue toolbox *(Nicholl/Adkin).*

of the drum; the chassis for both models was a trolley type for the first and a wheelbarrow type for the second, both with two wheels, first of iron and later, rubber-tyred, with a metal stand.

However, in the fullness of time and progress from piston to turbine, these useful old pieces of equipment were replaced by a multi-purpose re-fueller, the Pressurised Field Replenisher Mk 3, still of similar design but updated in its supply method. Instead of the 50-gallon (228-litre) drum there were two oil containers of a total of 10 gallons (45 litres), the smaller capacity being indicative of the jet engine's low oil consumption, and connected by flexible pipes. The supply is pressure-fed either

A Fluid-replenisher Can Mk 3 of 10-gallon (45-litre) capacity for use on aircraft hydraulic systems and engine-oil reservoirs, in store at RAF Stafford, July 1986. Soon to be superseded.

Multi-purpose fuel bowser for refuelling ground equipment – power units, petrol, diesel, etc. – at RAF Valley, September 1992.

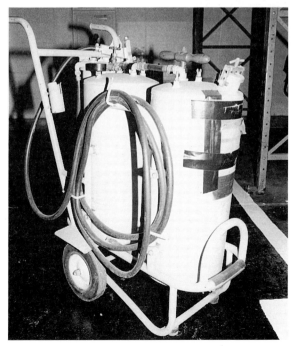

A Fluid-replenishment Trolley Mk 1 with a 150-gallon (684-litre) capacity tank to supply oils, de-icing fluid, etc. This unit shows the modern styling. RAF Cosford, September 1986.

That essential item when refuelling or starting aircraft engines – the foam extinguisher. RAF Valley, 24 September 1992.

by hand pump or by an external compressed-air supply at a constant pressure. Oil (or hydraulic fluid or de-icing fluid) is fed from the containers via a micro filter and 19ft (5.8m) of hose to a delivery gun and to the aircraft system through an appropriate adaptor. Operating pressure is 40–45psi (2.8–3kg/sq. cm), observed on a gauge on one of the mountings. The chassis is still a two-wheeled trolley. Weight is 116lb (52.6kg).

It is when the big passenger and freight aircraft are turned round and serviced that one can appreciate the proliferation of GSE units and the modern aircraft's dependence on them. Taking a service VC10, for example, the following units may be positioned around the aeroplane separately or in groups (see page 89):

- Refueller(s)
- Toilet trolleys
- Oxygen trolleys
- Hydraulic servicing rig
- Catering truck
- Fork lift
- Low pressure air starter
- Air conditioner trolley
- Water bowser
- Electrical servicing trolley
- Steps
- Baggage truck
- Crew and passenger vehicles
- High-pressure air-servicing trolley
- Fire appliances
- Cleaning units

These units are positioned according to their connecting points, access/exit of passengers and freight, and the safety areas. The modern passenger

aircraft's general description as an airliner can be seen to be relevant.

As fighter performance increased in the years after WW1, more attention was paid to the problems of high-altitude flying, the major one of which was keeping alive and efficient in the oxygen-restricted heights above 15,000ft (4570m). Much of the research was into developing satisfactory breathing apparatus and the use of pressurised suits and anti-glare aids. The real eventual beneficiaries of this were the ordinary squadron pilots and aircraft crews and eventually the ordinary passenger, in having more efficient oxygen systems. Before and during WW2 these comprised a number of oxygen bottles usually mounted in the fuselage and connected by suitable piping to a distribution point, from where the oxygen was piped to crew positions for their use.

The standard method was quite suitable until WW2 brought in more aircraft with larger crews to fly higher for longer periods and so require oxygen on an ever-increasing scale during their operational sorties. To maintain maximum consumption, the number of oxygen bottles required per aircraft rose tremendously, which led to a great increase in the number of replacements/spares needed to hand, or in stock each day. Increase in the number of aircraft per establishment and squadrons further brought the demand for more instrument trades to service and replenish these oxygen stores. With an operational station having around 30-40 Lancasters or similar aircraft on operations each night, each aircraft requiring oxygen bottles and systems to be serviced, in addition to other phases of instrumentation, one may appreciate the instrument trade manpower problems alone. So another method to reduce manpower tasks was speedily required.

It came, far too late to affect the last war, in the form of the oxygen charging trolley, based on a modified bomb trolley and designed to carry four

A B2 test stand sited in RAF Valley workshops, used for
testing and setting oxygen regulators for various altitudes.
September 1992.

A Zwicky nitrogen servicing unit which converts liquid
nitrogen to high- and low-pressure gas for use directly on
to the aircraft. RAF Valley, September 1992.

Early WW2, possibly pre-war, air compressor with a single-cylinder petrol engine. Much used in the early days for dope/paint spraying. RAF St Athan, May 1986.

high-pressure (HP) cylinders, which fed individually discharged oxygen into a common manifold, from where it was fed under control to the aircraft charging point. Oxygen bottles in the aircraft were changed only when necessary. The trolley was towable and steerable and fitted with brakes. Early models carried three cylinders and were also mounted on a two-wheeled chassis. The oxygen trolley worked well and has stayed in service, usually with four 2000psi (140kg/sq. cm) cylinders. The use of HP oxygen with this method was superseded to some extent by the introduction of liquid oxygen (LOX), which is now used in many aircraft systems.

For this method a revised equipment was devised, the replenishment liquid oxygen trolley, again based on a trolley chassis, but instead of separate gas cylinders a special insulated vessel of 40-gallon (182-litre) capacity was fitted, equipped with a control panel and the necessary valves and gauges for filling the vessel from a fixed storage-tank installation. The oxygen is transferred in its liquid form from the trolley, under valve control, via a special hose into the aircraft's vacuum flask type tanks. The vessel holds the equivalent of 5590cu. ft (158.3cu. m) of gaseous oxygen at 60°F (15°C) at a LOX working pressure of 50psi (3.5kg/sq. cm). A safety relief valve blows off at 60psi (4.2kg/sq. cm). The trolley chassis incorporates a towbar cum brake which operates when the towbar is either on the ground or in a vertical position. This piece of equipment has been superseded by a modernised version

containing fully enclosed comprehensive controls and gauges mounted on a steel chassis with two large-diameter tyred wheels, with full bumper protection. Replenishing these trolleys from bulk storage is a two-man operation and stringent safety precautions are necessary.

Air at one time was only what the aeroplane flew in, its only use for many years, other than aerodynamically, being to fill out rubber inner tubes. This remained the case until the introduction of the first air and oil oleo legs, and Dunlop and Goodyear devised their air-operated brakes. For the tyres all that was needed was a foot- or hand-operated pump capable of raising a pressure up to 50psi (3.5kg/sq. cm). Pneumatic brakes did not become a satisfactory system until an air compressor was fitted to, and operated by, the aircraft engine and was able to maintain a pressure of 200psi (14kg/sq. cm) in an air reservoir, from which the brakes drew their supply at 80psi (5.6kg/sq. cm). The new concept of wing-mounted guns discarding the restrictive – in terms of rounds per minute – oil-operated interrupter gear in favour of compressed-air operation, was another use for this medium. The reservoir was still supplied from the engine-mounted compressor, but with the pressure increased to around 400psi (28kg/sq. cm), and could be recharged or topped up from an external source, such as an early mobile engine-

A High-pressure (compressed air) Air Charging Trolley Mk 2A, 2B, 2C, with four 4000psi (281kg/sq. cm) cylinders at RAF Cosford in September 1986. These units have been largely superseded by nitrogen sets.

A Broomwade Air Compressor trolley with canopy removed, on servicing at RAF St Athan, May 1986.

The insides of the Broomwade, giving some idea of the work involved for the various GSE trades. RAF Stafford, July 1986.

A lightweight tactical air compressor in use at RAF Valley, September 1992. It was designed for field use and is air-transportable.

driven pneumatic trolley which was introduced for the higher air-pressure systems.

The GSE used to service air systems followed the same systematic development as most major serving GSE, beginning between the wars with a double air-cylinder machine using a two-handled rotary pump. This 1920s model was replaced by one of the earlier powered mechanical air pumps, the Air Compressor Trolley type G Mk 4, 5 and 6, a simple single-stage compressor driven by belts from a single-cylinder petrol engine and used for topping up air bottles and tyres, including MT use. It had an output of 2½-3cu. ft (0.085cu. m) per minute at a pressure of either 100 or 350psi (7.03 or 24.6kg/sq. cm). The mechanics were mounted on a two iron-wheeled chassis which weighed approximately 560lb (254kg).

The trend from the beginning for these pneumatic servicing trolleys was for them to be general purpose machines and in that they were very successful and still are. One or two had the supplying of compressed air for aircraft servicing as part of their output and one such, which was an interim type, was the Low Pressure Air Pneumatic Servicing Trolley Mk 2, introduced in the 1950s. This was a versatile unit and was used for general workshop purposes in addition to the above. It is described in detail in Chapter 10, but mention is made of its output of 20cu. ft (0.566cu. m) of free air per minute at 200 psi (14kg/sq. cm). Weight was 1588lb (720kg).

Compressed-air replenishment away from a hangar supply has been provided by a series of GP compressor units or compressed air cylinders and special units for direct aircraft supply. The GP trolleys, usually under the nomenclature of High or Low Pressure Pneumatic Servicing Trolleys, are used to supply air where no static compressed-air lines are available and service such operations as pneumatic tools, tyre inflation, paint spraying, engine inhibiting, etc. In this chapter, for the replenishment of aircraft on turn-round, one of the first supply units to do this job quickly and efficiently was the High Pressure Air Charging Trolley Mk 2A, 2B and 2C, used for air systems and missiles. It was very similar in appearance to the oxygen-charging trolley in that the chassis was a modified bomb trolley and carried four HP air cylinders, each of 4000psi (281kg/sq. cm) maximum, in the cradle. The cylinders connected through a central manifold and charging regulator with valves mounted in a steel control box at the rear and by a single hose to the aircraft or missile-charging panel. The trolley was towable.

In the course of development the inherent dangers of fire and explosion in the use of compressed air have largely been eliminated by substituting nitrogen for those tasks where the fire/explosion risk is greater, e.g. in fuel tanks.

The heavy aircraft of the war years, carrying up to ten aircrew over long distances on operations where the availability of toilets was a prime factor, had seen the vital necessity of efficient sanitation and all such aircraft were equipped with chemical closets. These had to be serviced and were normally emptied into a large container, cleaned, refilled with the chemical and returned to service, all well and good, but not a pleasant job. Pre-war civil airlines had, of course, similar toilet facilities. The advent of the York, a large passenger-carrying aircraft, increased the demands on sanitation facilities, together with interior passenger cabin cleaning, with the consequence that later passenger transport maintenance decreed the need for a much more efficient and less

unpleasant method of dealing with sanitation servicing.

A start was made with the Aircraft Toilet Servicing Trolley Mk 3, albeit originally meant for the ground servicing of self-flushing toilets in VIP aircraft. The method, and the self-flushing toilets, was extended to equip all transport aircraft. This useful piece of GSE comprised a 50-gallon (228-litre) sump tank, 14-gallon (64-litre) slime tank, 8-gallon (36-litre) charge tank, a 24V battery-operated pump and a control panel and an emergency hand pump, all mounted on a towable wheeled chassis.

The sewage was drained by gravity from the aircraft toilet system through a flexible funnel fitted to the sump tank inlet, and the trolley front castor wheel was retractable to allow the trolley to be tipped to press the rubber top of the funnel against the aircraft to form a seal around the sewage outlet; the trolley was held in this position by a prod fitted in the drawbar. Water was then pumped in from the sluice tank, through a 1in (25mm) hose connection to the aircraft, to flush the toilet system, which was then charged with chemical solution from the charge tank. The passage of the water and solution was controlled by a regulating valve and time switch.

Aircraft cleaning trolley for general use. It is comprehensively equipped and mainly used for transport aircraft. This unit was in store at RAF Stafford in July 1986 and shows the cleaning compartment at one end.

A similar type of cleaning trolley, slightly different in layout and fully equipped with cleaning utensils and materials for general cleaning of transport aircraft. Photographed from the opposite angle to the unit left, to show liquid-container storage. This unit was also in store at RAF Stafford in July 1986.

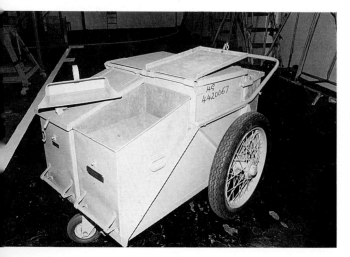

An obsolete Heavy-duty Vacuum Cleaner Mk 1A in use at RAF Mountbatten, servicing marine craft in 1985.

The solution consisted of ¾pint (0.426litre) Rascan disinfectant fluid per gallon of water. A 6in (15.24cm)-bore drain valve in the base of the sump tank was fitted with a quick-release valve and was used for draining the sewage into a ground manhole. The trolley tanks had sufficient capacity to service five aircraft toilets – not much, but a step in the right direction. The later Mk 5 is used on the big passenger jets and is more than adequate.

Among the GSE used on the Transport Command staging posts was the Aircraft Cleaning Trolley, hand moved on a two-wheeled chassis and looking rather like a park attendant's barrow. These were for en route aircraft only and were fitted with containers for disinfectant, water, closet waste and dry waste. They also carried a comprehensive range of cleaning equipment, which included two galvanised iron pails, two scrubbing brushes (still in use), two WC brushes, a bannister brush, Flit sprayer and a dustpan. The washbasin water tanks were also topped up. LAC Mopps was well catered for, even more so when interior cleaning went mechanical and a heavy-duty Vacuum Cleaner Mk 1A was put into service. This was a mobile vacuum cleaner driven by a single-cylinder petrol engine mounted on a two-wheel towable chassis fitted with four stabilising rods. The engine drove a turbo exhauster to create the vacuum through either of two connected 30ft (9m) hoses. A set of tools was included and the weight was 1064lb (482kg).

A less heavy but more sophisticated vacuum cleaner is the Panther, designed originally for service aircraft. The unit is soundproofed and self-contained with its collection container integral with

A Sturtevant Panther vacuum cleaner being demonstrated on a Hercules aircraft. This cleaner is still in service (Sturtevant Engineering Co. Ltd).

a fabricated exhauster, all mounted on a hand-steered three-wheel chassis.

Early hydraulic systems were replenished by the traditional method of pouring in the correct fluid from a scrupulously clean container up to a prescribed mark on the tank and checking the filter cap was clean and fitted correctly. With the very high operating pressures that developed in later aircraft systems the circuit was sealed and as a result replenishment is now done using the pressurised fluid can. The Mk 2 version can also be used for replenishing de-icing systems and engine oil reservoirs and comprises a 2-gallon (9-litre) container, pressurised by double-acting hand pumps to feed the fluid via a flexible hose and delivery gun. The can is fitted with a pressure gauge and is in all respects similar to the earlier Mk 1, except for the diameter of the delivery hose. A range of adaptors is supplied for connecting the delivery hose to an appropriate system. Weight of the can is 360lb (163kg).

Illustrating the night conditions and lighting which are now normal in RAF operations, particularly on the transport routes. To supplement inadequate lighting on those stations not so well equipped, or for special night-time operations, mobile floodlighting has been extensively developed. This scene was at RAF Fayid in the Egyptian Canal Zone in 1948 and shows a Bristol Britannia being serviced en route to the Far East *(R. Honeybone/Adkin)*.

Two Simplon Trailalite Mobile Floodlight Trolleys Mk 3 at RAF Stafford in July 1986. These particular sets were used at RAF Stanley during the Falklands campaign. The generator is in the box.

A mobile floodlight Skylite Mk 1–2 by Henry Gooch, which provides high-intensity temporary floodlighting and replaced the Simplons at RAF Stanley. RAF Brize Norton, June 1987.

That most vital item of an aeroplane, its tyres, appear to receive the least attention, but of course this is not so. It is a tribute to the tyre manufacturer that so little servicing appears to be needed, where in actual fact much research and development has been, and still is, put into these mundane-looking objects. The basic rubber and the materials with which it is impregnated have been appreciably helped by the design of the multi-wheeled bogie undercarriage, which materially spreads the great loads and high landing speeds of the heavy jets on to the few square feet of surface contact. But occasionally one tyre will blow, whether on a large aircraft or a small, and for that eventuality on most stations complete spare wheels of the aircraft types operating from the station are always standing by for a quick wheel change. A wheel is normally carried on a

Webster portable lighting set used on Bloodhound radar sites in store at RAF Stafford in July 1986.

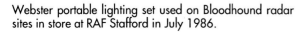

A Hylite lighting trolley with power-unit generator and full mobility in store at RAF Valley, September 1992.

A Skylite lighting trolley used for lighting parking areas, loading bays, etc. Mobile and fitted with its own generator. RAF Valley, September 1992.

two- or three-wheel metal trolley/wheeled stand, sometimes secured by a chain or bar to prevent movement and usually towable. Some stations have made or modified an existing stand to suit their own requirements.

With the modern service aircraft operating at night as routinely as by day, much extra duty hours are called for in servicing Support Command aircraft – and others – staging through on routes. So, naturally, an efficient floodlighting scheme is required and on all stations handling night servicing this is installed on a permanent basis. On some of the smaller stations, or in times of crisis operations when no mains electrical supply may be available, efficient lighting sets have been designed for this eventuality. One such is the Simplon Trailalite Mobile Floodlighting Trolley, which included the Falklands operations in its use, and

comprises a folding pole at the top of which are mounted four quartz halogen lamps. The poles are carried on a two-wheeled towable trailer on which is fitted a generator box and cable drum and which carries the power supply unit and controls. A small example of the technical ingenuity displayed by RAF trades is in the case of an electrical servicing trolley on RAF Brize Norton which the WO i/c GEF had modified as an efficient temporary measure to supplement existing GSE floodlight trolleys. It mounts two quartz halogen floodlamps on the top surface with power supplied from the GSE's own power unit.

All these lighting units are self-contained in that the power unit is usually a petrol or diesel engine, driving the generator and complete with all necessary controls and instrument panel. Some of the units are supplied with telescopic poles for the lamps.

Chapter 7

Blow Hot, Blow Cold

Under a lowering January sky an icy wind blows across the aerodrome, hardening the ice packed along the hangar approach roads. Not an aircraft to be seen for, along with the erks, they are huddled in the draughty hangars. Essentially a non-flying day. Good. But no! Chiefie received instructions yesterday from OC A Flight to have two Gordons ready for 1000 hours take off. So Chiefie has laid on the MT heater van.

Nearly all aircraft of the period 1918–38 were hangared, with the possible exception of flying boats, whenever inclement weather was around, which meant anything from high, gusty winds to below zero temperatures (and overseas, shelter from blistering heat and dust) unless flying was urgently required. There is no doubt that most of the aircraft in service *could* fly in these conditions, but the very flimsiness of their construction (not against aerodynamic forces) and the fabric covering, decreed that they had to be pampered against the jarring vibrations of ice-hard ground, dangerous icing up of flying controls and the overall effects of freezing temperatures. Heat and dust also gave problems.

In WW1 freezing conditions affected all, both in the trenches and up in the pale blue sky, usually from the mechanical point of freezing machine guns and controls, just as field guns and transport could also freeze. Men? Well, yes, they could get rather uncomfortable. So there was usually a winter stalemate on operations. In the years between the wars, most of the RAF's brush wars and crises took place overseas in warmer climes and although it could be intensely cold on the continental stations of Iraq and the North-West Frontier of India, this wasn't a major problem. At home in the UK aircraft ops were usually suspended in icing conditions – many an aircraft had been lost until this phenomenon was understood.

It was the coincidental understanding of the problem, the outbreak of war plus all the acquired knowledge that was incorporated into the designs of the new aircraft that enabled operations in icy conditions to become the norm. Despite many teething problems, which all trades were concerned in correcting, the aircraft were kept in operational trim – as were the MT, marine craft, balloons, etc. during the periods of intense cold.

When required to fly in low temperatures a major pre-WW2 problem was the engine oil, which at that time had a far lower viscosity and would thicken considerably within tank and engine when cold. The early greases also tended to freeze in winter unless thinly applied. The oil in the aircraft tank was normally drained off overnight from the chosen aircraft and warmed up on a stove or forge in the workshop or contained in the oil bowsers which had the means of external heating. The judicious use of a blowtorch on a can of oil wasn't unknown. When the oil was warmed it was replaced in the aircraft tank and, to speed up the process on a very cold morning, the MT heater van was brought in to puff its pitiful supply of warmed air around the engine cylinders and possibly the cockpit. The van was a rather large affair carrying two large-diameter flexible hoses on the roof through which the heated air was blown via a hot-water radiator and petrol engine-driven fan. These vans stayed in use throughout the war years and their inadequacy was shown up both during the iron winter in northern France during the stalemate period of 1939–40, and during Icelandic winters.

Heater vans being at a premium and insufficient numbers being available in France, simple engine heaters were quickly designed to help warm aero engines (and the tradesmen working on them) and consisted of canvas covers secured over a light framework 'tent', completely covering the engine of

A Mk 4 ground-heater non-toxic trolley modified to blow air for venting purposes (aircraft fuel tanks, for example) at RAF Stafford in November 1986.

a Blenheim or Battle, and extended to ground level; inside was placed a safety paraffin heater to warm the engine (slightly). The odd erk found that beneficial, too, in addition to his new issue of one leather jerkin and permission to wear woolly pullies, balaclava and gloves.

To give an example of operating in extreme cold weather, the task of a meteorological flight based in Reykjavik in Iceland during the last war was to take off an hour before dawn every day, only dense fog excepting, to collect the meteorological data which was so vital to the war effort. This task meant preparing a Hudson at least one hour before take off, usually two, for in the intense cold of an Icelandic winter extra time was needed to warm the engines, substantially so when using the MT heater van. This van was essentially the same as that described with some criticism above, but fitted with three hoses, one of which was put into each engine

cowling and the third into the cabin; the output was on full delivery for at least an hour. But in the hangar was a small Canadian mobile heater which, powered by a small petrol engine and with one hose, could be handled by one man and delivered more heat than any two hoses of the van.

The heater vans remained the main source of external supply until after WW2 and their range of usefulness was extended to such important jobs as heating parachute-packing rooms. Also, the extending of the RAF's sphere of worldwide operations to the colder, often freezing, climes of extreme north and south via Transport Command opened up the need to keep standing aircraft as warm as possible by directing external warm air into cockpits and system positions such as navigation instruments and radar/radio installations. The need becoming essential, new heater units to replace the old MT vans began to come into service, beginning with the Ground Heater Mk 4.

This heater answered the demand for a greater output of British Thermal Units (BthUs) per hour by supplying 1300cu. ft (36.8cu. m) minimum at a capacity of 350,000BthU/hr by means of a Villiers

Non-toxic Ground-heating Trolley Mk 4. Supplies uncontaminated hot air for pre-heating aircraft engines and equipment, removal of ice, snow and frost, and heating of parachute-packing rooms, etc. Powered by a Villiers Mk 25 air-cooled engine. Heat capacity is 350,000BThU per hour with a maximum air delivery of 1300cu. ft (368.12cu. m) per minute. Can also be utilised to supply cooling air.

Khamsin Portable Heater Type D500 Mk 1. A portable space heater powered by a Petter AB1 diesel air-cooled engine, producing 3000–5000cu. ft (849.5–991.1cu. m) with a temperature rise of 270°F (150°C) above ambient.

air-cooled petrol engine, fitted with an impeller which drew air into a heating unit, into which fuel was pumped and the mixture ignited. This unit had the added facility that by shutting off the fuel supply the trolley could supply cold air. The mechanics of the unit were built on to a three-wheeled steerable chassis enclosed by steel panels, with provision to mount two hoses and stow these on the top. The trolleys were later adapted to blow non-toxic air, thus widening their application to supplying air into the passenger cabins of transport aircraft. Weight was 700lb (318kg).

The technique of cold weather operations was of increasing importance with the RAF's post-war commitment to NATO on the northern flanks where all-weather flying exercises are the norm. To this end GSE was designed to make the task easier and the van and trolley heaters were supplemented by such units as the Khamseen (hot wind) Portable Heater type D500 Mk 1, a portable space heater, with the possible heating of offices or workshops in mind. The unit was introduced about 1970 and was powered by a Petter AB1 diesel air-cooled engine, which produced an output of 3000–3500 cu. ft/min (85–99cu. m/min) at a temperature increase of up to 270°F (132°C) ambient temperature. It was a compact unit and weighed dry 550lb (249.7kg).

The constant preparation and training for the unwanted probability of action in extremes of cold conditions have naturally led to increasing development for this eventuality. One of these was the Aircraft Heater Trolley Mk 7 Apollo, made by

A publicity photo of an Apollo aircraft heater Mk 7 shown in use on a Jaguar. This type of heater was extensively used in the Falklands after the campaign *(AMSS)*.

Apollo aircraft-heater trolley used to good effect at RAF Stanley and highly acclaimed by its users, including those on domestic sites. This model is at RAF Cosford for servicing, September 1986.

An AMSS Gemini aircraft heater which utilises many parts of the Apollo Mk 7, shown here in a publicity pose *(AMSS)*.

AMSS, which was used to supply heated air to aircraft interiors and equipment. This heater was to prove its worth in the aftermath of the Falklands conflict when, on Stanley with the occupying British forces, it was also used extensively to heat the men's accommodation and domestic sites at a time when no other suitable heater was available. It was highly acclaimed and did a magnificent job during the rebuilding of Stanley and its large airfield complex. The success of this heater led to the introduction of the Gemini, which utilised many parts of the Apollo but was more compact.

The Gemini has incorporated all the lessons that had been learned from the Apollo and the unit, although 'run-of-the-mill' in appearance, reveals a surprising versatility and is a successful attempt to produce a multi-purpose machine that, in effect, could reduce the numbers of this type GSE in service. As its official nomenclature indicates, its primary purpose is to provide heated air at 2000cu. ft (56.6cu. m) per minute either for aircraft interiors or in general use where required. The 'where required' factor leads to the first of its versatility

points, for it is easily air-portable as an underslung helicopter load. To extend that facility, a detachable snow sled is available for such areas as have been mentioned above.

As one might expect in that area in winter, some means of additional lighting is often necessary and this the GSE provides with its own multi-directional floodlighting from two tungsten halogen lamps. Keeping in mind the areas in which the unit may operate, the engine designers have foreseen the possibility of difficulty of supply and given the diesel engine multi-fuel capability, using diesel, Avtag, Avtur, Jet A1 or paraffin on which to run for a maximum of eight hours. An extremely useful unit, the Gemini is also a source of electric power, with a total generated capacity of 5kVA, for the operation of hand tools, vacuum cleaners, etc., and can be run from an available mains supply. The mechanics are enclosed and are mounted on a two-wheeled chassis, towable and fitted with an adjustable jockey wheel. The unit is fully instrumented and weighs 375kg.

The present GSE in use include the aforementioned and the Mk 5, which delivers non-toxic air, is made by Flight Refuelling and turns the scale at a high 1588kg. As might be deduced from the layout of these heater trolleys, it is but a small step

Tornados of the Tri-National Tornado Training Establishment (TTTE) at RAF Cottesmore, with full covers on, similar to pre-WW2 standards. Note the starter trolleys between the aircraft. The occasion is RAF Cottesmore's fiftieth anniversary as an RAF station, 11 June 1988. The author's 35 Squadron was one of the first two to occupy Cottesmore in 1938.

A flight-refuelling air-heating trolley Mk 5 at RAF Brize Norton, used to deliver non-toxic air to aircraft interiors. June 1987.

Defrosting Fluid-spraying Plant. One of the early spray plants for defrosting the external surfaces of aircraft, used in the early 1950s. It consisted of a portable tank, a hand pump and a 6ft (1.8m) spray pipe with three alternative lengths of hose. A first development of the original stirrup pump.

for a designer to make units which produce cooling air, a series of which have seen service and are considered as important for the modern aircraft as are the heaters.

The declaration of war in 1939, with its expectation of immediate bombing, had all operational aircraft dispersed out in the open, placed head to wind and secured by the between-war method of picketing. The wheels were chocked fore and aft and large, corkscrew-shaped iron pickets were screwed into the ground at points just off each wing-tip and near the tail wheel. Picketing rings, an aircraft item, were screwed into wing-tip sockets and a rope attached, with a degree of slack, from the aircraft picketing ring to the ground picket. The tail picket was roped to the tail wheel fork. The aircraft's control surfaces were secured and the brakes applied, if possible.

To give the aircraft some measure of protection from the elements, manufacturers had devised – on pre-war standards – and produced sets of aircraft covers, of which the Fairey Battle is an example. A set included propeller, mainplane, cockpit, wheels and tailplane covers. All very well for the rain but virtually useless operationally in frost, snow and ice, because of their icing up solid by the following morning, with the consequence of the near impossibility of unlacing the frozen securing cords. A more suitable method of combating quickly, easily and cheaply had to be found to resist the ice and snow effects, particularly to those aircraft not so protected, and Kilfrost was born.

The single largest contribution to cold-weather operation, Kilfrost came in two forms, paste and liquid. The de-icing paste was first applied generally by hand of the mechanic, sometimes with the help of a wooden spatula, to the leading edges of tail and mainplane of those aircraft not fitted with the warm-air de-icing boots. This method of application was not conducive to a satisfactory aerodynamic airflow over the surfaces, which became critical on the high-speed fighters and some fast twins, and it was virtually impossible to expect cold erks to maintain by hand the thickness of paste recommended by the maker along a 40ft (12m) leading edge, particularly when the pressure was on to get the aircraft airborne on a cold and frosty morning. Before this method was introduced, if aircraft had been left out and collected a coating of frost, snow or ice, the only means of dealing with it was to use a sweeping brush, occasionally with a mixture of ethyl glycol and water – which was somewhat similar to earlier anti-freezing liquids for motorists – and, if available, hot air.

Then Kilfrost produced their famous liquid, which superseded the paste. This was applied with a bomb Blitz type of stirrup pump; the sight of airmen armed with such a pump spraying frost- and snow-covered surfaces became a common sight on RAF aerodromes and was an effective and long-lasting solution. The well-used stirrup gave way after WW2 to a defrosting fluid spraying plant, the first piece of GSE specifically designed for this work, and more suitable in that it was a hand-operated portable tank and mobile like a wheelbarrow, with a choice of 10, 20 and 25ft (3.04, 6.09 and 7.6m) hoses to which a 6ft (2m) spray pipe could easily be fitted for use on a variety of aircraft. The weight of this small unit was 46lb (21kg).

To keep pace with the larger aircraft entering service, a custom-built vehicle, the power-operated aircraft defrosting plant, was introduced in the early 1960s. This unit comprises a four-wheeled trailer chassis on which is mounted an access tower; the platform can be adjusted from 8ft 6in to 13ft 6in (2.6–4.1m) to suit the aircraft. A Villiers engine drives a horizontal hydraulic pump, which delivers 4 gallons (18 litres) of Kilfrost fluid per minute from a 100-gallon (454-litre) tank at a pressure of 300psi (21kg/sq. cm). The tank is heated for a hot fluid method from a 400/415V three-phase electrical supply. Equipment accessories include spray guns, spray lances and extensions, standpipes and filling

Power-operated Aircraft-defrosting Plant. A trolley used in the 1960s for the defrosting and de-icing of heavy aircraft. The fluid was heated from a 400/415V three-phase electrical supply and delivered through lance-type spray guns by a Villiers Mk 20 engined and powered pump. The equipment was mounted on a four-wheeled chassis which incorporated an adjustable-height access tower.

hose – and four bass brooms to brush down the nice smooth highly aerodynamic surfaces!

Probably the definitive aerospace ground equipment for the de-icing and defrosting, using the latest Kilfrost methods, of large aircraft is a bigger version of the defrosting plant. This machine has a large capacity tank in which the Kilfrost can be mixed and heated, circulated by an electrically operated centrifugal pump and maintained at its operating temperature of 203°F (95°C), mounted on the rear of a six-wheeled, forward cab truck chassis. The centre section of the chassis is fitted with a Simon hydraulically operated adjustable boom which carries the trained operator, hose lances and control platform; the boom has a working reach of 75ft (23m). When in use the plant has two hydraulically operated stabilising pads which are extended on either side of the vehicle, which weighs in at 51,740lb (23,470kg).

With these machines the importance of de-icing has reached its zenith. The use and application of various Kilfrost fluids has become an essential service, backed up by custom-built mechanisation. The techniques of operating the mobile plant for the

application of the fluid, with the plant having its own maintenance manual, indicates how far this science has travelled from the old stirrup-pump days.

Winter operations were not all about aircraft de-icing. The runways and taxi tracks had to be cleared and for that there were the standard MT operated snow-ploughs, which all did a good job. There were also the airmen and their shovels to whom recourse was taken when and if MT was not available or to complement the snow-plough; for this extra fatigue it was usual before and during WW2 to revive the airmen with a tot of service rum, but mugs had to be of ceramic, as enamelled iron mugs would tend to corrode! The period when the V bombers were in service was one of full alert standby for very fast take off, which became something of a legend, but not much use if the runway was only partly cleared; the early snow-ploughs then in use were not as efficient as they are today, so a much faster and revolutionary means of clearing the snow and melting the ice was sought to get the V bombers away.

The resultant machine, although MT-operated, is described, as it required the use of aircraft engine tradesmen to maintain. The idea of using a jet engine for this work was not new – it had been tried out on the railway about 1948 during an extremely bad winter to clear the railway points; some experiments had also been carried out using it as a method of runway clearing. The result was the introduction in the early 1960s of the runway de-icer, of which only a few were produced. This machine was a sturdy fabricated platform chassis fitted with three castoring wheels, one centrally mounted at the front and one at each rear corner. Mounted on the chassis was a central control cabin with a De Havilland Derwent Mk 8 gas turbine engine on either side, the jet effluxes facing forward and fitted with flat nozzles to spread the heat over a wide pattern. The cabin contained engine controls, instruments, VHF radio and intercom for the de-icer operator to communicate with the driver of the 2500-gallon (548-litre) refueller which was chosen as the prime mover, or pusher. The cabin was also soundproofed against the noise of the two jet engines and to allow the radio to be heard. But the prime mover was not soundproofed and the driver of that had to endure the additional noise of his diesel engine; sound levels in the driving cab were recorded at 114 decibels at RAF Bruggen in 1977. The refueller also carried the fuel for the jet engines.

A mobile heavy-duty defrosting and de-icing plant used with Kilfrost products and shown near a TriStar of RAF Brize Norton in June 1987. The plant has a 75ft (23m) reach and is made by Simon Ltd.

When operating the de-icer over bad surfaces an injudicious use of the throttles could cause out-of-balance sliding. This was later rectified by mounting the engines to balance out the thrust and by a two-point fixing between de-icer and mover. The de-icer was very extravagant on fuel, but the price was considered worthwhile during the V bomber period because of its undoubted speed and efficiency at clearing ice.

This machine was superseded by more modern and fuel-efficient snow-ploughs such as the Sicard which can clear most runway debris as well as snow. A late-model runway de-icer is based on the crop sprayer, with folding spray arms to suit conditions, and incorporating a tank for the de-icing fluid. Another method which was also expensive was the use in the early 1970s of UREA granules as a means of de-icing. These, spread at the right time – a couple of hours before the temperature actually reached freezing – prevented a wet runway from becoming a sheet of ice. It also stopped snow from freezing to the runway surface, thus making snow removal easier. The method required the use of standard highway gritters to spread the UREA and several services were introduced to load the gritters, including a grain screw hoist.

For those (solitary) erks who feel left out of the action, the RAF has in service a pedestrian rotary blower, the Snowbird S263. Although designed for one-man operation for use on footpaths and station roads, it is probably pressed into runway/taxi-track service on occasion. Its operation is conventional, a single-cylinder air-cooled engine driving a fast fan which ejects the snow from an adjustable positioned chute.

Royal Air Force aircraft range much of the world, but by reason of Britain's geographical position and past Empire – now the diminishing Commonwealth – the major routes were through north and central Africa, Egypt, Aden, Malaysia and Australia, with staging posts sited in some of the hottest and most barren areas, such as Lagos, El Adem and Mauripur. In the earliest days, before WW2, both air and ground crews just sweated it out on the old stations of Kohat, Basra and Mosul, for example, seeking solace from the heat in any available shade, tired old fans stirring up the hot air to one degree less, waiting for tiffin and a chance to charp off the

A runway de-icer of the 1960s, which utilised two Derwent gas turbine engines to supply hot air for defrosting and de-icing the runway. The photo shows the front of the unit with two jet effluxes and the control cabin. This unit was awaiting disposal at RAF Cosford in 1987.

Runway de-icer showing the three-wheeled chassis and rear of the control cabin. RAF Cosford, 1987.

Runway de-icer with its prime mover, usually an AEC Mammoth Major refueller, which also refuels the jet engines.

Close-up of the attachment coupling of a jet fuel tanker prime mover. The communication cable to the vehicle cabin can also be seen.

heat. Often the aeroplane's wings were the only source of shelter. Early cabin aircraft depended on a primitive make-up of forced ventilation, involving a combination of louvres, windows and canvas sheets, which was only spasmodically successful, depending on wind strength. Servicing the aircraft, be it fabric-covered biplane or all-metal monoplane, working in temperatures of 120°F (49°C) plus, meant a real risk of skin burns. During the war large numbers of servicemen endured the heat, humidity, dust and dangers of the desert campaigns for years at a stretch, working with minimal ground equipment, which fortunately in most cases was as rugged as the aircraft to stand up to the conditions. And then came the transport aircraft to replace ancient Victoria and Vernon.

At first these mostly comprised the Bombay and Harrow, still very basic inside. There was no cooling system, but as all aircraft were much the same, all passengers were equal in their discomfort. To replace these old types came the ubiquitous Dakota/DC3 – there was no finer aircraft for the conditions of the time – followed by the first Avro Yorks, with their superior furnishings which brought out the need for an external source of cooling air. In the first year of its operation this aircraft carried mostly VIPs who did not take kindly to being left in a sweltering cabin on the ground while the aircraft was being routinely serviced, and so were cosseted by being taken to an artificially cooled accommodation on the theory that an over-heated (or frozen) VIP does not function properly. The Yorks were joined after the war by Hastings and civilianised Lancastrians and Valetta aircraft, whose complement of passengers increasingly included ordinary civilians and servicemen with their families staging through to new postings.

The need to cool the cabin on the ground while engines were stopped was always apparent, not only for servicemen, but to ease the physical distress caused by the sudden transition of a family from the damp chill of a British winter into a 90°F (32°C) plus

A Sicard 4½-ton snow-removal unit, used for both snow and dirt clearing and normally towed. In general use on most home RAF stations.

A late-model runway de-icer based on an agricultural crop sprayer, shown with its arms folded and attached to a towable bowser. Also shown is the warning lamp *(RAF Stafford print)*.

atmosphere with up to 90 per cent humidity. On some staging posts local rules were such that all passengers had to stay aboard during turn-round, enduring the delights in the stifling heat of a local man spraying the hot interior with an anti-something or other.

The first of the cooling GSE had the advantage that existing heater trolleys, despite having a heater unit instead of a refrigerator/heat exchanger, could be, and were, relatively easily adapted for cooling. The Hastings, Valetta and Comet and others of a like ilk, flying the route stages very much quicker and so speeding up the effects of a climate change, soon indicated that a more advanced cooling unit was becoming a necessity, not a cosseting. The sophisticated electronics for instrumentation and radio/radar were at first sensitive to extremes of heat and the high humidity in places such as Aden further accentuated the need for on-ground cooling. And, sinisterly at that time, a period of increased hijacking of airliners emphasised the need to make conditions tolerable for hostages held inside an immobile metal shell in fierce Middle Eastern sun.

The more modern types of aircraft have their own heating and cooling systems, but these generally operated only in flight conditions with the engine(s) running. On the ground it all came to a stop,

although on newer aircraft auxiliary power units are now installed to operate these systems where ground equipment is minimal. Before this, cooling and heating arrangements had to depend on an external source of supply for their operation, and still sometimes do.

Among the first GSE to supply cooling air to an aircraft interior and vital areas of certain instrument systems was the pressure cabin and air-cooling trolley, introduced in the mid-1950s; it also supplied heating, fumigating and deodorising. Power was

Two views of a Mk 5A air-cooling trolley showing: above, some of the plumbing and engine drive belts; and below, the heat exchanger and fan drive. The unit is mounted on a mobility base. RAF St Athan, May 1986.

Pedestrian-operated Rotary Blower (Snowbird S263). Designed for clearing footpaths and confined areas, this unit is pedestrian-controlled with forward, neutral and reverse gears. The operation causes a fast-rotating fan driven by a Briggs and Stratton type 143302 air-cooled engine to eject snow from an adjustable chute.

Air-cooling Trolley Mk 1. To cool the interior and confined spaces of aircraft on the ground and supply cool air, a self-contained trolley was introduced. This unit was powered by a JAP single-cylinder petrol engine which drove a compressor and two fans of the refrigeration plant to give a maximum capacity of 24,000BThU per hour. The unit was fully enclosed and towable on its three-wheeled chassis.

Pressure Cabin Testing Trolley Mk 1C. Used for the testing of pressure cabins of high-altitude aircraft, this trolley was a small, two-wheeled type carrying a Marshall type J100 compressor driven by a JAP engine. Output could be regulated to give 30–110cu ft (0.78–3.1cu. m) free air per minute at a pressure of 2–10psi (0.15–0.70kg/sq. cm).

from a Rolls-Royce B81 Mk 5G petrol engine directly coupled to a Godfrey M2000/7 positive displacement blower. The charge air was supplied by the blower at 1500cu. ft (42cu. m) free air per minute at 12psi (0.84kg/sq. cm) for pressure testing, when required. For cooling purposes the cooling circuit air passed through two fan-cooled air-to-air heat exchangers and a Godfrey CA-9 Mk 3 cold air unit at 1860cu. ft (52.65cu. m) per minute at 0.5psi (0.035kg/sq. cm). When supplying air at ambient temperature up to 120°F (49°C), the unit gave a temperature drop of 90°F (32°C). Heating capacity was 300,000BthU/hr. All the equipment was mounted on a fully enclosed four-wheel chassis fitted with a drawbar and with front-wheel steering. Weight dry was 5336lb (2420kg).

A whole range of cooling units were developed by ML Aviation, beginning with the ML Coolair Minor, many still in service. These machines were originally designed for civilian use and adapted to RAF needs. The Minor became the Air-Cooling Trolley Mk 1 and was generally used for cooling cabins, with some ability to cool confined spaces where system installations tended to get hot. The unit was self-contained and delivered air through the medium of a refrigeration plant via an air-cooled

twin-cylinder JAP model 55 petrol engine and two fans driving a compressor. Cooling air from the Mk 1 was delivered at 400cu. ft (11 cu. m) per minute at 55–90°F (13–32°C) ambient temperature and was of 240,000BthU/hr capacity. The plant was mounted on a three-wheeled towable chassis with sheet metal and wire-gauge protection. On the top of the unit was stored two 8in (20cm) diameter flexible hoses.

A very similar-looking and operating Mk 2 was produced and used for providing cool air to assist ground running and testing aircraft radar installations. There were technical differences, mainly in the Mk 2 having a Rootes supercharger which overcame back pressure caused by narrow circulating paths in the aircraft equipment, and a larger fuel tank to give longer continuous running. Weight of both marks were also similar, that of the Mk 1 being 1555lb (705kg).

From these two air coolers stemmed a line of ML cooling units and the development in this particular field became one of degree. As aircraft increased in size, complexity and sophistication, so did the cooling units to service them. ML Aviation supplied a succession of units which became Marks 3, 5 and 7 and which had alternative power plants of petrol and diesel. They became automatic in operation and reached at least 560,000BthU/hr capacity in the

A Keelavite air-conditioning trolley Mk 9 at RAF Brize
Norton in June 1987.

A Coolair unit Mk 6 in use on a BEA Comet in the early
1960s (ML Aviation publicity photo).

A Normalair-Garret air-conditioning trolley servicing two
Jaguars on a dispersal pan *(Normalair-Garret publicity
photo)*.

An ML Aviation Coolair unit Mk 5-5A shown servicing a
Vickers Valiant in 1960 *(ML Aviation publicity photo)*.

Mk 7. The trolleys extended in size to six-wheeled trailers of 17,023lb (7720kg), a somewhat rapid increase from the Mk 1's 1555lb (705kg). Of course, passengers and crew benefited greatly, which was the aim of the exercise but, as with most GSE of this type, more static units were added to those cluttering the tarmac, needing an MT prime mover for mobility.

Chapter 8

Armaments

Despite attempts to portray it otherwise, often caused by the obviously attractive lines of some models, the military aeroplane is not designed for the glamour that has been appended to a few well-known makes; it is strictly functional, and away from its natural element much of it is expensive junk. The fighter and bomber aircraft's job is to deliver destruction in as quick and efficient a manner as possible; they are gun platforms and long-range artillery respectively, although the distinction is becoming rather blurred, as from these two types stem variations of the theme, ground attack, night

Make do and mend or Get off your bike! This print shows the ingenuity of adapting existing and available items to the usage of war. A DH9 and an old fuel bowser are shown at the rear *(Royal Aeronautical Society)*.

Poor print of a pre-WW2 front gun synchronisation instructional layout for use with biplanes, in this case the Gloster Gauntlet of 17 (F) squadron in about 1937 (Nicholls).

fighter, dive bomber, etc., all carrying weapons appropriate to their function. The servicing of these armaments requires a trade as busy and technical as any in the major aircraft trades and potentially more dangerous.

The armourers could possibly be the oldest of all trades, their services first enlisted when a dinosaur bone needed to be fashioned into a club, or flint spears required renewal. Whether or not, the devotees of this thriving trade have hardly been short of work since. The trade has also developed into a responsible (strangely, in view of its end product) as well as a hard-working one. Responsible in that the operation of a field catapult, or a field gun, or a torpedo, had to be as reliable as possible. Hard-working in that those same machines were heavy and the ammunition used equally heart-straining, whether stone boulders or shells for the guns. And when the Royal Engineers took to the air it heralded a future of lugging guns, bombs and torpedos

around. Within the RAF the trade was to become even more demanding of intelligence and skills, as the machine gun and bomb gave way to rocket and long-range missile. In company with other modern trades the micro-electronic control and operation of armaments was to take precedence, but slowly.

With the evolution of the machine gun firing through the propeller, the gun-harmonising stand was probably one of the first true armament GSE. Introduced in 1917, it remained in use for all front guns mounted to fire through a propeller and designed to set up these guns to converge to a particular pattern at an adjustable pre-set distance forward of the aircraft. As machine guns increased in number and were mounted outside the arc of the propeller, they required a wider range of harmonising, as indicated by the Gloster Gladiator's two wing-mounted guns, the twelve-gun Hurricane 2C and the fighter version of the Beaufighter which mounted both cannon and machine guns in the nose. The later universal gun harmonisation stand allows for most arrangements to be set, including the heavy modern 30mm Aden cannon. The stands are also adaptable to harmonise camera guns with the machine-gun settings.

The stands consist basically of three boards mounted on tripod assemblies, for fuselage, port and starboard wings, each board adjustable for height and all interconnected by tie rods at the base with slide rails at the board positions for adjusting the sighting disc. The tie rods can be adjusted in length between 3 and 12ft (1.0–3.6m). Each board has provision for mounting sighting discs for gun sights, guns and cameras, and the whole equipment can be packed into three containers for air transport. There was the added work previously of setting up the early biplanes for front gun testing on the range, when the aircraft was put into near rigging position, the trestled tail firmly secured by rope to adjacent blocks and the wheels equally firmly chocked before the engine could be started and the guns tested in earnest. The gun range was a special, of course.

When the begoggled British ace swept out of the sun on to his German enemy and opened fire with his front machine guns (or vice versa), the rate of fire was dependent on the revs produced by the engine/propeller ratio, i.e. low-revving engine with high-geared prop, faster rate of fire from the cam mounted on the propshaft transmitting its impulses through oil pipelines to the Vickers gun breech.

A Hawker Hind of 12 Squadron rigged for front gun harmonising on the station gunnery range. The photo shows how the tail is trestled and secured to a concrete block set in the ground, with another to prevent tail movement. About 1937.

During the later part of WW1 when every fighter and most two seaters had a forward-mounted machine gun firing off its belts of ammo, the work of replenishing these was a full-time job back at the aerodrome, just as was the refilling of the Lewis gun pans. After that war, this kind of armament work carried on to a lesser degree in the Middle East and the North West Frontier of India where the RAF was operationally engaged, and it was always a full-time job, made longer by the time taken to align the rounds in the belt by hand.

It was not long before technical minds evolved mechanical methods of filling gun belts and placing the rounds in their correct position relative to their feeding into the gun breech. The breakthrough came with the invention of the link-type belt together with a hand-operated machine for filling the link belts in the correct sequence. The links, which separated as a round was fed into the breech, and the cartridge cases were at first considered expendable, until the showers of links and cases falling adjacent to RAF

gun ranges brought forth irate complaints and the price of brass went up! Modifications followed and the previously expendable items were guided into a receptacle in the aircraft. During WW2 spent cartridges were sometimes allowed to fall free. With the advent of the multi-gun fighter, belt filling became a major operation.

When the 20mm cannon came generally into service, a similar GSE to the hand-filling machine mentioned above, suitably adapted, was used to assemble and fill the belts which, after completion, were passed to a Hispano Belt Positioning Machine No. 2 designed to position 20mm ammunition in belt links. It consisted of a base on which was mounted a driving shaft and a tappet block which had seven spring-loaded tappets arranged cylindrically and which moved rearward successively as the shaft was rotated by a handle. The belt was fed into the machine from the left side and the sprockets engaged the cartridges and fed the belt through the machine when the handle was turned. The relative position of the round in the link was determined by the setting of the sprocket and the nose-adjusting cam fitted at the front face of the rear lever housing and by the operation of the tappets. Weight was 33lb (15kg).

As is well known, the criterion of a successful fighter beside its performance, or in spite of, is the

An array of the aircraft machine guns and cannon with which the gun armourer had to be acquainted. Aerospace Museum, Cosford, July 1992.

speed of its turn-round on the ground, of which rearming is vital to the sortie. To carve off valuable seconds the concept of the interchangeable gun pack has greatly eased the time factor and the armourer workload. The Hunter fighter was among the first to mount large-calibre cannon in a detachable pack which could be removed complete for servicing and rearming, a special trolley being used. This was the Hunter Gun Package Servicing Trolley, which also served as a mounting from which guns could be test fired. The trolley had a chassis frame shaped to form a gun-pack cradle which could be raised 6in (15cm) by means of a hand-operated hydraulic pump. Four screw jacks fitted at the chassis base were utilised to help secure the cradle on the firing range. The SWL was 2000lb (907kg) and the four-wheeled trolley was towable, with another towing eye fitted and four wheel brakes. Weight was 1502lb (681kg). A lighter,

three-wheeled GP version of the Hunter gun trolley, which served the same purpose, being hydraulically operated with the same amount of lift and also incorporating a fork-lift assembly, was in service use.

When the pack was re-armed the 30mm ammunition belt would have been assembled in a Positioning and Debelting Belt Filling Machine, Aden 30mm (phew!) which was capable of belt filling, belt positioning or debelting by the interchange of suitable components. The machine has a cast base on which the three bearing housings carry the actuating and sprocket-shaft assemblies and also provide the mounting for the gearing and operating mechanism. Various types of chutes are provided to cover the three operations. The machine weighs in at 1003lb (455kg).

The introduction of the gun turret increased the defensive capabilities and the fire power of operational aircraft. Their use at first relied on old-fashioned muscle power from the gunner – as in

An Aden 30mm cannon gun pack as used on Hunter fighters, RAF Museum, December 1983.

Aden Position and Debelting Belt-filling Machine. This hand-operated machine fills the belts, positions the ammunition or debelts Aden 30mm rounds.

Hispano Belt-positioning Machine 20mm No. 2. A hand-operated machine designed to position 20mm Hispano ammunition in belt links. The turning of the handle causes rotating sprockets to engage the cartridges and feed the belt through the machine; the relative position of the round is determined by the sprocket settings and a nose-adjusting cam.

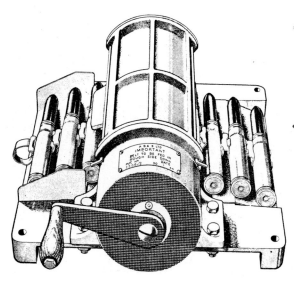

Aircraft Gun Turrets Maintenance Stand Type B. A stand used to support aircraft gun turrets for all stages of servicing, testing and firing and for training purposes. Of tubular steel construction with interchangeable seating rings to suit the various types of turrets. The stand had four castor wheels and four adjustable stabilising jacks.

the Boulton and Paul Overstrand – until they were made more efficient by the introduction of hydraulic power. The turret was another item for specialist servicing and this was usually carried out *in situ*, more often at dispersal. Because of war pressures to keep aircraft serviceable, human errors occasionally occurred, sometimes with fatal results from turret manipulation while carrying loaded guns. Gun-turret servicing also presented a problem both because of the close confines when working within a turret and the limited ability to operate one inside a hangar. So a special stand was designed within which a turret under servicing could be placed for repair, testing and even firing. The Maintenance Stand type B – Aircraft Gun Turrets – could also double as a training aid. This tubular steel stand had interchangeable seating rings at its top for mounting the particular type of turret under servicing, screw jacks for stabilising and four castor wheels for ground movement. For any work which involved movement of the turret a standard hydraulic servicing trolley could be used to supply the hydraulic power.

The very effective 60lb (27kg) rockets which came into use during WW2 and which were electrically fired from underwing launching rails developed after that war into air-to-air missiles, either heat-seeking or radar-orientated. They gave a highly sophisticated addition to the armourer's repertoire and technically placed him well into the top trades. For the handling of these missiles, special hand-pushed stands were used for transporting and to arm an aircraft the missile was installed by being slung from a cradle bar and manipulated by a hand winch similar to a bomb winch, but which carried an extension to allow the operator greater accuracy.

Other missiles came into service, some on a short-lived basis, like Blue Steel, which required expertise of a high order and Bloodhound, a surface-to-air missile which was at first semi-mobile but over a very long period of thirty years became fully mobile and air-transportable. Bloodhound's biggest disadvantage was that, in addition to the launcher, it required two cabins containing the control and electronic systems for receiving enemy aircraft signals and transmitting launch data and controls; although a mobile missile, it took an appreciable time to set

A transportation trolley for a Bloodhound ground-to-air missile Mk 1 being developed for display purposes at RAF St Athan in May 1986.

An AVRO Blue Steel air-to-ground guided bomb on its
transportation trolley on display at Manchester Air and
Space Museum in May 1983.

A 1960 THOR intermediate-range ballistic missile mounted
on part of its mobile trolley at the RAF Museum at Hendon
in December 1983.

An early version of the Bloodhound surface-to-air missile on display at the Aerospace Museum, Cosford. The radar set of the Bloodhound missile complex (and it is) which relays signals from the target to . . .

. . . the control cabin in which signals are collated and analysed and distributed to individual missile sites for . . .

. . . the firing or launching of the chosen missile. The later types are fully mobile with operating control units much reduced in size. The box object at the left of the cabin in the middle picture feeds cooling air to the complex electronics.

up. Bloodhound was not technically an aircraft missile, but was, of course, maintained by armourers with a high degree of technical expertise and by rocket-motor fitters. It was never fired in anger, but in addition to being a useful deterrent it gave modern armourers much technical training. The nose cone, packed with electronics, required electronic technicians. Blue Steel was a one-off and had a long life, but it also required servicing of a high order with much specialised ground equipment.

Up to the advent of the new monoplanes there had been little need for anything stronger than, or mechanically superior to, the very primitive 'wheelbarrow' type bomb transporter that had been a long-serving relic from the First World War. Bombs for biplanes rarely exceeded 250lb (113kg) in weight; most were 112lb (51kg) and they were manhandled on to the external bomb racks. Now, the height and capacity of the internal bays plus the wartime increase in bomber aircraft and their capacity required a more efficient bomb trolley, able to service up to three squadrons of twelve aircraft on one station for one sortie in a short time; if the aircraft were Whitleys, Wellingtons or Lancasters, that was a lot of bombs to handle.

The first standard airfield bomb transporter designed for use with the Expansion type aircraft, was all metal and intended to carry bombs, or stores as they were known in the service, from 1000 to 10,000lb (454–4536kg) and 2000lb (907kg) bombs. It consisted of a very low four-wheeled chassis fitted with detachable cradles made to suit the bomb weight and size required. Bombs could be winched up to the racks in their cradle, which would be detached after use; these were discontinued in later years. Hand-operated hydraulic jacks were fitted to give some degree of height adjustment to the chassis cradles when loading on to the racks. Front and rear steering was incorporated along with hydraulic brakes on all four wheels operated by a hand lever or an overrun mechanism in the towbar. Each trolley had a towing eye and hook, features which allowed a bomb train to be formed; these are usually seen in photos being towed by a Fordson tractor driven by a WAAF airwoman. From this standard type came a number of equally useful variants. The safe working load of the standard was 14,000lb (6350kg) with the trolley itself weighing in at 3115lb (1412kg).

One of the variants was the Bomb Trolley type J Mk 1 and 2, which was designed for transporting

A Bloodhound SAM on its transporter, Duxford, July 1983.

single large bombs and incorporated mechanical aids in loading and unloading these bombs, usually of 2000lb (907kg). The single store was carried, supported on rollers and steadied by hinged trunnion brackets, on a channel-section chassis, with the bomb nose protected by a guard rail. The trolley wheels, with hydraulic brakes, were under the main load-bearing section and the trolley had four screw jacks to steady and raise the chassis when loading and unloading an aircraft. This GSE could well have been the forerunner of the modern weapon loader and was a comparative lightweight at 860lb (390kg).

A special-to-type was the Canberra Bomb Loading Trolley Mk 1 and 2, which in its design took the mechanical operation of lifting stores from trolley to bomb rack a stage further than the type J. As they were custom-built the dimensions of operations were constant, making the work easier for the bomb armourer, as witnessed on Malta and Cyprus during the short-lived operations against Egypt in 1956. Both marks were similar in construction, with the Mk 2 having provision for coupling the hydraulic fluid supply line to the hydraulic pump on a motorised hydraulic servicing trolley, and also a different method of attachment at the elevating head. The trolley was able to carry bombs ranging from 16½ to 32in (42–81cm) diameter and elevate these up to the bomb bay by means of the hydraulically operated elevating head, which could be raised from a minimum height of 7½in (19cm) to a maximum of 4ft 8in (142cm). Max SWL was 5000lb (2268kg) and weight of the trolley was 3332lb (1510kg).

The weapon loader referred to above was a completely new machine, self-motorised and mobile, able to be adapted quickly to most types of aircraft bomb gear and stores by means of specific adaptor heads, although a number of marks were brought into service for specific aircraft use. The original concept was American, adopted by the RAF as the Weapon Loader type T. Its mode of operation was similar to the type J trolley in that it

'Special to type' STRABO crane for use with a V2 missile. A scissor mechanism at each end turns through 90 degrees and is then wound up to lift the horizontal beam to a height of about 13ft (4m). The crane can be operated either electrically or by hand and will lift 16 tons. Aerospace Museum, Cosford.

Three-wheeled unpowered trolley used for the transportation of Hawk aircraft rocket-launcher rails. RAF Valley, 24 September 1992.

Canberra Bomb-loading Trolley Mk 1 & 2. Custom-built, these trolleys are used to lift bombs from 16½–32in (42–81cm) hydraulically into Canberra aircraft, power being supplied from a separate trolley. The maximum working load is 5000lb (2268kg). The differences between the marks lie in the method of attachment of the elevating head and the coupling of the fluid supply line. Fully towable.

A standard Airfield Bomb Transporter carrying 250lb (113kg) bombs to load a Wellington aircraft at RAF Lindholme during the winter of 1940/41. The officer on the left is F/Lt Rushton, pre-war armourer NCO *(F/Lt Rushton)*.

A Martin Baker ejection-seat stand used for maintenance and on show at the Aerospace Museum at Cosford in September 1986.

Another view of armourers engaged in bombing up a Wellington and servicing the gun turrets prior to an operation from RAF Lindholme *(F/Lt Rushton)*.

Bomb Trolley Type J Mk 1 & 2. Used to transport 2000lb (907kg) bombs and specially made. All four wheels are hydraulically braked, the two rear ones being positioned halfway along the chassis to shorten the wheelbase. Screw jacks are fitted to raise and lower the unit. The 2000lb (907kg) store is steadied on the chassis by trunnion brackets and roller beams.

Standard Airfield Bomb Transporter. Designed to carry 1000–10,000lb (454–4536kg) bombs and 2000lb (907kg) mines on a four-wheeled chassis by using various cradles. Chassis ground clearance can be adjusted from ½–6½in (1–16.5cm) by hydraulic jacks and the chassis is equipped with towing bar, front and rear steering, and brakes.

Bomb Trolley Type F. A bomb trolley that differs in its construction from those above, but has similar controls and equipment.

was designed for individual stores. The chassis comprised a split-type two-girder beam front, each beam carrying twin, wide-tyred wheels. From a rear-mounted cab, to which the beams were attached, projected the hydraulically operated loading arms with the bomb-type attachment head required. The cab rode on its driving wheels and was fully equipped, with all controls mounted on a fascia panel. By use of these controls the store could be lifted and manipulated to mate with all-in service bomb gear. Maximum lift was 7000lb (3175kg).

From the Mk T evolved several British modified marks, R, V and W, all doing a similar job but varying in number of road wheels, actuating arm, adaptor heads and mobility drive, though marks R and W were more compact. They were a great asset for the V bombers and were later modified for use on the Tornado, Jaguar and Buccaneer.

In conjunction with the trolley method of loading and unloading was the vital bomb winch, usually portable and mostly adaptable, of which there were a number of types to cover all bomb-carrying

A weapon loader type T, used for loading bombs on to aircraft. Various types are used for different aircraft. This one is in a bad state of disrepair and will probably be scrapped as obsolescent. RAF Stafford, July 1986.

The control panel of a type T weapon loader. Control levers are shaped to represent function and as an aid to operation at night. RAF Stafford, July 1986.

The working end of a type R weapon loader. The end fitting is basic to type of store to be fitted and can be changed quickly. RAF Stafford, July 1986.

A weapon loader type W awaiting disposal at RAF Stafford in July 1986.

Type R weapon loaders stacked in storage awaiting
disposal at RAF Stafford *(Official ST/446/93)*.

In the foreground, Type W weapon loaders in storage at
RAF Stafford after renovation. These loaders were used on
Phantom aircraft.

This type W weapon loader is a greatly modified version of the original. RAF Stafford, July 1986.

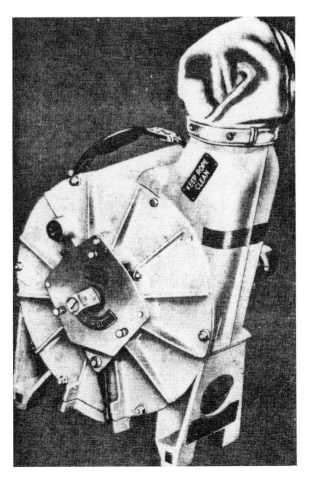

aircraft. The (usually) hand-operated winches were designed to be attached to some part of the strengthened bomb bay; when in use a locating piece was inserted into a socket at the required bomb station of the bay. One example is given as typical of most, although there were the special-to-aircraft types. The 4000lb (1814kg) bomb winch for fuselage bomb bays could be operated either by hand or driven electrically or hydraulically, which made it very versatile. It comprised a cable drum, clutch and brake and weighed 88lb (40kg), rather heavy to be used by hand. A somewhat similar machine, using the same principles, is employed for loading air-to-air missiles, such as the Firestreak.

Inevitably, whether by mischance, technical errors, pilot error or by the hand of the armourers, an aircraft would crash and have to be salvaged, which ensured more grief for the ground trades and the use of specialist GSE.

Bomb Winch 4000lb (1814kg). A portable winch for use in fuselage bomb stations of aircraft and either hand-operated or driven by an electric or hydraulic drive unit. The winch comprises a cable drum, ratchet wheel, clutch and brake.

Chapter 9
Salvaging

The Blenheim had to be retrieved from rough, undulating ground deep into well-wooded country about four miles from an unclassified road. When the salvage team reached the aircraft, which lay on its flattened belly, its cabin crushed and one engine torn out, an ambulance had removed the unfortunate crew. The aircraft was returning from ops, was fully armed and had one 250lb (113kg) bomb still on its rack in the bomb bay. The salvage team comprised a Senior NCO (SNCO), two corporals (Cpls), four

tradesmen, three aircraft hands general duties (ACH GD) and a medical orderly.

With two trucks carrying their equipment they reached the nearest spot on the road from where the SNCO and a Cpl trudged to the salvage site, to

Some examples of the kind of work that salvage teams face. This is a Bristol fighter in a quite normal attitude for its day.

DH10 E906 has port engine cut on take-off at RAF Abu
Suir, Egypt, in 1920 *(F. Marchant)*.

A Hawker Audax, probably of 20 Squadron, overshoots
the landing strip at Miranshah, NWFP, during Waziristan
operations *(J.P. Murray)*.

weigh up the problem. Fortunately, the ground was firm from the summer and the SNCO decided the trucks might make it to the site: he sent the Cpl back with these instructions. While waiting for the team he studied the aircraft to decide on his *modus operandi*, what equipment would be required and (roughly) how long the job might take. The other engine would have to come out, the wings be removed and the tailplane dismantled. To enable all this to be carried out the aircraft would have to be raised to a working height and here the firmness of the ground was helpful. The Sgt estimated two full working days, which meant two nights under canvas; he had been notified that there were no handy farm buildings nearby, which meant a guard roster for the three ACHGDs and Corporals.

The two trucks, rocking heavily over the rough surface, ground on to the site and the Sgt set the men to unload and erect the two tents. Jacks and trestles, toolkits, stands, shovels, sleeping and cooking gear was stacked until the tents were erected. The SNCO instructed an MT driver to have the depot lay on a Coles crane for early next day and sent him off in a truck. As soon as the gear was stowed in a tent the Sgt used the remaining daylight to start the tradesmen dismantling the aircraft.

First and foremost the ammunition had to be removed and the aircraft disarmed under the control of the armourer tradesman. The hung-up bomb could not be defused until access was gained to the bomb bay and as a result the men observed much caution to avoid jolting it. The ACHs were informed of the seriousness of their guarding to keep all at a safe distance; to help in this a temporary rope barrier was put up.

With the onset of the evening, the airmen relaxed, sorted out their personal gear, made their beds, organised meals, chatted and read. By 2300 all had retired to bed. By 0600 all were being shaken awake to start another long day. And salvaging began in earnest.

The picking up of bits and pieces of aeroplanes began with the first attempt at flight and has continued ever since. Mostly all that was needed to salvage the early aircraft were a few strong men and a horse and cart or a flat-topped lorry. This essential exercise increased steadily in proportion to the increase in flying until, with the very large numbers of aircraft that had to force land, or crash, during WW2, the job became a specialised one and had ground equipment specifically designed for it.

One must not forget that salvage often took place

This Fairey Battle might present a problem to the salvage teams.

in out-of-the-way corners of the country, on hills or in forests or streams, as well as in numerous wheatfields and overseas deserts and jungles. The saga of salvage retrieval from difficult country has created mini epics of difficulties overcome by ingenuity, stamina and hardship that require telling if the story of this difficult work by ground-crew trades is to be made complete. Salvage teams are drawn from ordinary skilled tradesmen who become expert only through experience and confidence in teamwork. Some instruction on the peculiarities of specific aircraft types is given, either at a technical training school or the manufacturer's works.

The three years prior to WW2, with the need for high-intensity aircraft operation combined with familiarisation with many new types created the unfolding period in which salvage work developed its new techniques, administration and organisation. All this proved to be of enormous value when war came. The high aircraft casualty rate also saw the period when the design and production of new ground and salvage equipment was put into production. World War Two marked their coming of age.

Until then it was the job of the aircraft's squadron to send out teams to retrieve the aeroplane, which was invariably damaged; then a decision was usually made either to dismantle the aircraft and return it to the squadron, or to write it off as too badly

The aftermath of a serious crash showing the number of people who might initially be involved. After this stage, salvage can begin. In the background is a Coles crane that will be very busy removing the major pieces. Place, date and incident unknown.

damaged. In the latter case any useful items – instruments, guns and so on – were removed.

While, given the comparatively simple type of construction of the early days, it was quite easy to dismantle an aeroplane, the terrain it was in and the conditions existing could cause major problems. In shell-pocked earth within range of enemy guns, for example, dismantling could be more interesting than one might wish. A nice cosy meadow near to a farm was infinitely preferable. The remains were usually brought back by an aircraft tender, which itself could be a sight to remember on the roads of France or the Middle East.

In the beginning salvaging was fairly straightforward and fell, as today, into two broad groups of operations, either a forced landing or a real crash. For the first the essential thing was to get it off the site of its landing under its own power back to base if at all possible, by carrying out the necessary repairs *in situ*. This usually entailed specialist equipment. If the aircraft could not be repaired quickly or could not be flown off after repair, then it was dismantled and the fuselage usually towed behind a flat-bed lorry, on which would be stowed wings and other bits and pieces. A crash of one of these fragile machines usually meant a complete write-off and salvage was expressed in terms of saving what items could be re-used, subject to safety factors, and sweeping up the rest, which might mean several trips in order to clear the site. Domestic requirements such as tents, sleeping and cooking gear, salvage equipment, guards, remained basically the same for many years, with refinements in detail only.

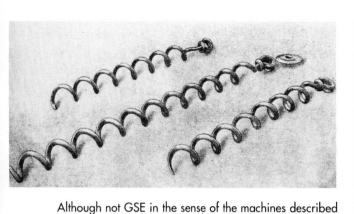

Although not GSE in the sense of the machines described in this book, these are an essential item in a salvage team's kit for securing aircraft in the open in bad weather. They are made in various lengths, widths and weights from high-tensile steel and used with the ground plates shown.

Two mobile aircraft-repair trailers used for battle damage (or non-operational) repairs. Not often required, but ready for instant use. RAF Valley, 24 September 1992.

During the inter-war years salvage developed into a fine art, in the sense that it was necessary to pay court to the great god, Economy, and most of the work became true salvage. Aircraft were dismantled very carefully in order that the aeroplane could be got back into the air as quickly and as cheaply as possible. In the early years it was the parent unit that collected the aircraft if it was within reasonable distance from base; alternatively the job fell to the station workshops of the nearest RAF station. The equipment of the day for salvaging was the minimum: the trusty sheer legs, ladders, trestles, wing stands, some specialist manufacturers' toolkits, a flat-top trailer with the necessary MT, a few shovels and muscle power and experience. If the salvage team was to be among the first on the scene it might take along an ambulance and a medical orderly if a gory problem was anticipated.

Again, as in practically the whole field of GSE it was the advent of the Expansion period aircraft, and very soon the opening of hostilities, that altered the whole tempo of salvage work. The all-metal aeroplanes hit the ground more solidly, were heavier and more difficult to retrieve and required a more comprehensive range of quick removal gear as it is sometimes known – although it was years before they got this. First among the contributing factors was the vastly increased flying training with its numerous prangs. After war was declared there was the great expansion of Flying Training Schools and commands, the French débâcle after 10 May 1940, although it is fair to say that very few crashed or force-landed aircraft were salvaged in France – there was little time for that – but the event in which salvage teams made a major contribution to getting damaged aircraft back into the fighting was the Battle of Britain. From that period it was a matter of steadily increasing retrievals throughout the operational commands.

As most salvage operations are to collect aircraft that have usually landed with their undercarriage up, the first major problem was how to lift the aircraft sufficiently to get a wheeled flat-top low trailer, or loader, under the fuselage or wing in order to raise it. A popular early WW2 method was to try different forms of jacking under the centre section or mainplane, which might involve digging a pit deep enough to allow a jack to operate. A useful item here was the Lever Trolley Jack type A and B, an 8-ton (8.12-tonne) hydraulically operated cantilever type, which had a minimum height of 10in (25.4cm); with a suitable extension head this could be increased to 1ft 8in (51cm). Lift of the cantilever was 4ft 6in to 6ft 5in (1.37–2m) with extension, and two flanged runways were provided – essential items for use on

WW2 vintage Tracjac still in use and housed in a special 'crash' equipment bay at RAF Valley, 24 September 1992.

soft ground. If it was possible to get a crane into place then of course this would be used in preference, subject to possible damage incurred in lifting. First among this range of new and efficient salvage equipment was that godsend, the Coles crane, mounted on a Thornycroft chassis, along with its stablemate the Queen Mary, a specially designed 38ft (11.5m) overall semi-trailer destined to perform meritorious service before, during and after WW2.

Having raised the aircraft it was necessary to place a trolley of some kind under it in order to move it; one such during the war years was usually an adapted bomb trolley inserted under the mainplanes, terrain permitting. A greatly improved logical development of the bomb trolley is the Tracjac Salvage Trolley, which requires only that the centre section or mainplanes be jacked high enough to pass the Tracjac under, about 3ft (1m). The Tracjac comprises a padded lifting beam and a jacking unit mounted on a steel chassis having two free-running tracked units. The jacking unit, which consists of two double-ram hydraulic jacks, is mounted between the tracked units and supports the lifting beams. Track tension can be adjusted by altering distances between axles – horizontal on front axle, vertical on rear. The hydraulic lift of the beams is 3.28ft (1m) with a maximum SWL of 18 tons (18.29 tonnes). Towing speed with maximum emergency load is 2mph (about 3kph) and the weight of one Tracjac is 5376lb (2439kg). A smaller, similar Main Salvage Trolley type C incorporating a fixed square wooden platform instead of a hydraulic beam is also used, with a maximum load of 10 tons (10.16 tonnes) and is primarily designed for use in removing aircraft from runways.

The worst situation that could occur on any busy airfield, more so on operational stations, was for a crash on the runway or taxi tracks with other large aircraft standing off with low fuel tanks, which would necessitate them being diverted to another airfield. For this contingency a specialist main salvage trolley was introduced, with the largest

The modern equivalent of a flight toolkit, where every item is booked out into a loan book, necessary in these days of economy. And a vital safety factor from lost tools.

aircraft in service in mind. Designed to carry weights up to 75 tons (76.2 tonnes) and be air-portable, the trolley consists of a flat 30 x 13ft (9.1 x 4.0m) platform chassis with four twin solid-tyred bogies, the front and rear pairs linked by Ackerman steering so that the trolley can be steered from either, or both, ends from a tiller to which a 10 or 50ft (3.04 or 15.24m) towbar can be fitted. The trolley can also be towed sideways after turning the bogies through 90 degrees. Air brakes are fitted and, very importantly, the trolleys can also be operated over some soft unprepared ground with support tracking. When in use it is designed to complement the 15-ton (15.2-tonnes) nose salvage trolley. The weight of the main trolley is 33,376lb (15,140kg). A high load-lifting crane is also required.

The nose-salvage trolley's primary purpose is to support the nose of aircraft that suffer collapsed nose wheels. It will support aircraft weight at that point up to 15 tons (15.2 tonnes); its secondary purpose is to be used in conjunction with the main salvage trolley. It consists of a four twin-wheeled chassis upon which is mounted a wooden 6 x 6ft (1.8 x 1.8m) turntable platform rotatable through 360 degrees: the chassis is steerable by a tiller to which either a 10 or 50ft (3.04 or 15.24m) towbar can be attached and is similar in other respects to the main salvage trolley. Its weight is 6384lb (2895kg).

Salvaging aircraft is not always a well-defined operation conducted by the book, particularly on operational units overseas. The author's experience during a detachment with his squadron to Asmara in Eritrea in 1950 illustrates the kind of minor salvaging job which can suddenly arise, a situation most aircraft trades NCOs have experienced. Due to high altitude problems (Asmara is at nearly 8000ft/2438m), two out of three Mosquitoes swung on take-off and swiped off their undercarriages, leaving a total strength of five NCOs and airmen to get the aircraft off the field. This was accomplished by using the Tracjac method detailed above, digging under each nacelle to insert the station's only two Tracjacs. A helpful army scout car did the essential towing; the work was 90 per cent physical, its only saving grace that of being on the station and not out in the 'mutti'.

Aircraft size and weight outgrew the Queen Mary era until the salvaging of aircraft in the Victor/Vulcan/VC10 size became an operation of immense and intricate complexity and, in the case

The ubiquitous prime mover of that well-known and essential set of MT for salvage, the Bedford. This one is towing a 'Queen Mary' aircraft trailer.

A 'Queen Mary' aircraft trailer, built in 1941 and an essential part of a salvage team's kit. This version was modified to carry the Spitfire. Seen at Newark Air Museum in September 1988.

of these aircraft, added security problems. In addition there was the urgency to remove any large aircraft from a runway. Larger and more updated salvage GSE, of which the RFD air bags are an example, was needed and provided.

One of the best innovations which drastically advanced the method of lifting an aircraft with the minimum use of heavy mechanical equipment is the RFD Low Lift Air Bag. The 'low lift' refers to the air pressure required to inflate these bags from the minimum of 6in (15cm) required to pass them into position under the mainplane or other parts of the aircraft – a great improvement over the former lever jacks, although these are still in use. Lift of the

air bag is dependent on the number of sections per bag – about 6ft 4½in (2m) for one unit comprising nine woven nylon elements independently bonded together to form a stack assembly. Air is pumped in via a control panel, from any external pressure source such as an air supply trolley or similar compressor, at a pressure of 3 or 7psi (0.211 or 0.49kg/sq. cm) respectively for a lift capacity of 24,000 to 56,000lb (10,886–25,400kg). The air bags are designed to operate in temperatures of –22° to +158°F (-30° to +70°C) and can be packed into a valise 7ft 3in x 6in (221 x 15cm) which weighs 350lb (159kg).

With modern aircraft, as with the older, it is often necessary to remove major components of the aircraft during the course of salvage to make the overall task easier, and for this the necessary stands are required. There are now many of these; most stands are custom-built for a particular type of

A DH Mosquito of 13 Squadron being towed from the scene of its 'ground loop' by a tracked infantry vehicle in 1950. The aircraft is mounted on two Tracjac salvage trolleys.

Main Salvage Trolley Type C. Similar in principle to the Tracjac, with a square wooden platform mounted between the caterpillar track units. Used for the removal of heavy aircraft from runways, it has a capacity of 10 tons.

Tracjac Salvage Trolley. A much-used and efficient trolley for lifting heavy aircraft, designed to be used with a towing vehicle. It comprises a lifting beam, jacking unit with two double-ram hydraulic jacks mounted between the track units, the track units and supports.

Nose Salvage Trolley 15 Ton. Used for removal of aircraft with collapsed nose-wheel assemblies. It comprises four twin-wheeled chassis supporting a 6 x 6ft (1.8 x 1.8m) turntable platform which can be turned through 360 degrees. The Ackerman steering at the front axle is operated by a tiller.

Main Salvage Trolley 75 Tons. This platform trolley is designed for the removal of large aircraft from airfield runways. The chassis is mounted on four four-wheeled bogies which are linked with Ackerman-type steering operated from a tiller. The unit can be towed sideways and may be dismantled for air transportation. It is designed to be used in conjunction with a 15-ton nose-salvage trolley.

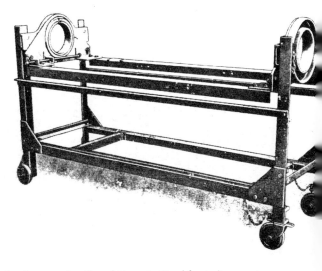

Engine-erecting Stand Type A. Used for in-line engines to enable it to be turned to any rotated position along its length for servicing. A drip tray is fitted.

engine or mainplane, or for radio/radar sets, for example. Prior to the advent of the jet aircraft many of the engine stands were 'universal' types and some of these are described. According to type one of the following two stands might be required.

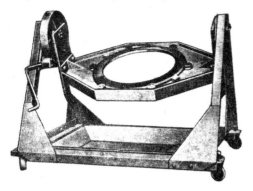

Radial Engine-erecting Stand Type C. Designed to support a radial engine for major servicing by turning to any desired position. Various adaptors are available and a drip tray is fitted.

For the in-line engine, such as the Napier Lion and Rolls-Royce Kestrel, the Erecting Engine Stand type A was a rugged structure which saw long service and was eventually adapted to take the Rolls-Royce Merlin. The engine bearers were designed to allow the engine to be turned for access and, like the radial stands, a number of adaptors were available to take a few selected engines. It incorporated a drip tray in the stand base and was simple and comparatively light in weight, scaling 896lb (406kg).

For the radial type of engine the Aircraft Radial Engine Erecting Stand came in several types. The type C was designed to support a radial engine during dismantling and erection when used at base, but for salvage work different adaptors were available to allow the mounting of a range of engines. As for the in-line, a deep drip tray was fitted. The type D was a basically similar stand with the emphasis on Centaurus engines, for which it carried a special adaptor. All stands were mobile on four castors and the type D weighed 1500lb (680kg), 450lb (204kg) more than the type C.

Closing stages of a salvage operation on a DH Mosquito. The team are preparing to bring in the aircraft on two Tracjac salvage trolleys, one under each retracted undercarriage nacelle.

Six stages in the use of RFD air-filled salvage bags on a real-life operation, showing the inflating equipment and points of support (all RFD):

The salvage bags being positioned under a mainplane in their deflated form. The bags will then be connected to the air manifolds in the foreground.

Air bags under pressure applying lift to the mainplane.

This view shows the inflation manifold from which hoses
are led to individual bags. In the background can be seen
the high-pressure air trolley which feeds the required air.

A general view of the aircraft, which has overrun the
runway and is being retrieved by the use of these inflatable
salvage bags.

A view of air bags placed under the rear fuselage and backed up by a tail trestle while the bags were being positioned.

RFD salvage bags under a wing, showing the individual inflating hoses to each bag.

Fitters servicing a Napier Lion in a type A Engine-erecting Stand. The stand was modified to accept Merlin engines and therefore had an extremely long life *(Print MOD H501).*

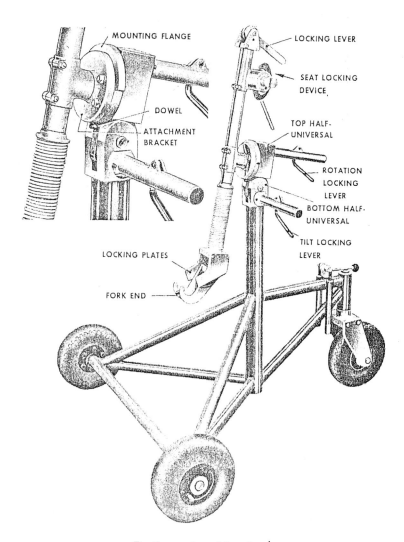

MOUNTING FLANGE

LOCKING LEVER

SEAT LOCKING
DEVICE

DOWEL

TOP HALF-
UNIVERSAL

ATTACHMENT
BRACKET

ROTATION
LOCKING
LEVER

BOTTOM HALF-
UNIVERSAL

TILT LOCKING
LEVER

LOCKING PLATES

FORK END

Ejection-seat servicing stand.

Nearly all modern cockpit service aircraft are fitted with Martin Baker ejection seats as against cabin seats, and this life-saving seat owes its efficiency to a controlled rocket expansion to eject the seat clear of the aircraft. That same cartridge is held in check of inadvertent firing by trigger safety pins, both of which have to be in position whenever the aircraft is on the ground. Unless properly handled by a skilled tradesman, the seat was a potential danger to personnel and it subsequently became mandatory to remove it on any servicing which involved cockpit occupation. On a salvage operation the seat was one of the priorities for removal; when this was done it

was placed on a Martin Baker Seat-Servicing Stand. The stand is a welded steel framework mounted on a three-wheeled chassis and the seat can be placed in five lateral and three vertical positions. Two adaptors are provided, one for use with Mk 4 seats; for use with earlier marks of seat the attachment mechanism consists of a spring-loaded hook which locates on the bottom cross shaft of the seat and two plungers which secure the side beams. The stand is light in weight and easily portable.

In these days of very high-speed landings from the fighter jets (when is the Harrier technique going to

A Lightning of 92 Squadron demonstrates in practice the effective use of a Safeland Arrester Barrier at RAF Leconfield. Compared with what could be, the damage caused by the cables is minimal *(Bruce Robertson Collection)*.

A Tornado of TTTE RAF Cottesmore after engaging an RHAG on an exercise *(Official)*.

be incorporated into other new aircraft?) brake failure can be catastrophic. To ease the results of such a failure somewhat and assist in the rapid removal by the salvage teams of a possibly damaged aircraft from the end of the runway, the RAF has adopted two separately designed systems of arresting an aircraft whose brakes have failed.

The Safeland Arrest Barrier is a net of reinforced ropes into which a fast-moving aircraft is quickly and progressively slowed to a halt by the braking energy required to spin an air-braked fan. The rotary hydraulic arrester gear (RHAG) is by a cable laid across the runway much the same as an arrester cable on an aircraft carrier with each end of the cable attached to a hydraulically controlled large fluid flywheel-type drum mounted in large mobile trolleys. The braking action is by the energy being absorbed by the fluid flywheel retarding the run of the cable. (See page 168.)

These appliances are protective items rather than salvage; that requirement may come after the arresting aircraft has been stopped.

A Rotary Hydraulic Arrester Gear (RHAG) unit in store at RAF Stafford, 24 September 1992. Two units are needed when the system is in use.

The inertia-operated cable drum of the RHAG at RAF
Stafford, September 1992.

Chapter 10

Deep Servicing

All RAF aircraft equipment is maintained according to a routine servicing cycle which ensures that every item is checked and/or serviced. In contrast to the earliest days, when maintenance of ground equipment was done on a 'as required' basis, the complexity of GSE now demands a depth of maintenance previously given only to aircraft. It has also always been RAF policy to maintain its machines in a clean condition and as soon as the peace of 1918 arrived this policy was rigidly adhered to. The early biplanes were issued with centre-section mats which consisted of a series of wood slats attached to large squares of canvas and were used to protect the fabric surfaces during refuelling and servicing, soon to become a necessity from the maintenance point of view, as post-war economics decreed that equipment was going to have to last more years than expected.

This sound philosophy led to pre-WW2

Washing a Tornado by pressure detergent with a Steam-cleaning Plant type A. Note the airmen standing on the tailplane, which must be quite rugged. RAF Cottesmore, June 1987.

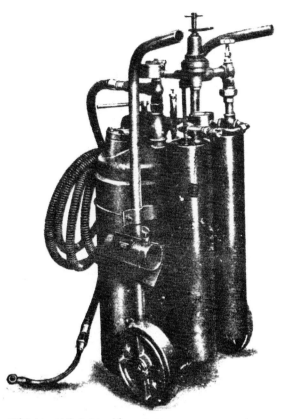

Oil Primer Mk 2. Used for priming aero-engine oil systems before an engine is started after draining, installation or storage. The primer is operated by compressed air held in two vessels and charged externally from a hand or foot pump or from a pneumatic servicing trolley.

squadrons devoting Saturday mornings to scrubbing down aircraft, in which all flight personnel – junior pilots not exempted – were expected to participate with some enthusiasm. The equipment was simple – bar or liquid soap, buckets and scrubbing brushes, rags old cleaning and elbow grease. There were occasional bursts of cleaning during the war, usually of the essential kind, but cleanliness became an essential activity after the advent of the jet aircraft. It became a vital aerodynamic factor for the very high-speed Meteor and Vampire, whose smoothness of surface was a contributory factor to their performance. Cleaning was taken to extreme lengths, scrubbing brushes were out and a special polish was introduced. It was calculated, with factual evidence, that any accumulation of dirt and dust could seriously affect flying qualities and top speed. Sometimes protection mats were used.

However, in the light of experience gained, whereby performance of Hunters and similar aircraft seemed unaffected by ground crew treading over the mainplanes, it was apparent that the use of polish – developed for the world speed record Meteor – had been an extreme for ordinary squadron aircraft and with the use of better, harder paint finishes, the old faithful soap and water method was back. But real progress was made in cleaning when the chore went mechanical. The Steam Cleaning Plant type A took out all the previous elbow grease and nearly ruined shareholders in liquid soap manufacturers! The plant provides a jet of high-pressure steam for removing dirt, oil, grease, etc., from metal surfaces and it was mounted on a manually moved three-wheeled chassis. It was universal, being applicable also for MT, marine craft and heavy machinery. The plant used a 230/250V single-phase motor to power a pump which supplied a mixture of water and degreasant solution (a source of new shares?) to a kerosene-heated steam coil, where a wet stream at about 100psi (7.03kg/sq.cm) was generated and passed through flexible hoses to two cleaning guns.

Oil-filling Rig Type 11565. This rig is used for priming and draining items of equipment which use silicon fluid or water glycol as a cooling medium. It comprises a silicon fluid tank, an electric motor driving a hydraulic pump, a filter, drain and pipe valve, priming and draining hoses and a detachable water glycol tank. This is all mounted on a two-wheeled steel trolley. The electric motor is operated from a 220/250V or 380/400V supply.

An obsolescent turbine-compressor washing rig up for scrap at RAF Stafford in July 1986. A later mark has a nitrogen cylinder installed for charging and is also used on helicopters.

The ground crew welcomed this one. In the natural course of events later models, working on the same principle, were completely mobile, larger and mounted on a truck chassis.

Once inside the hangar the aircraft was usually jacked up and the inspection begun. For the pre-WW2 period equipment was minimal, usually the tradesman's toolkit, grease guns, any special spanners etc., ladders if required, a small mobile steel workbench with a vice, racks for cowlings and panels, small floodlight-type lamps, air pumps. If the fabric was to be opened up then the repair tools, thread, wax, fabric, dope and brushes were wanted. If the engine(s) had to be removed a prop stand was needed along with the mobile crane and engine stand. If that engine was going to be in store for some time, it was usual to prepare it by inhibiting the cylinders.

Formerly this was done by injecting engine oil with a syringe through the plug holes and turning the engine over to ensure the oil covered the cylinder walls. The great increase in numbers of modern engines and their protection against corrosion when in stored conditions brought in the rust-preventative sprayer, which was used for spraying the inside of the cylinders with corrosion inhibiter by means of a hand pump mounted on the body of the sprayer, and a spray nozzle fitted with an off/on cock.

Wartime operations with piston engines under adverse climatic conditions revealed the need to protect their interior against corrosion if they were going to be stored for any length of time, or had been drained of oil. This became apparent when new engines from both the UK and the USA were brought into service after a lengthy storage period or, in the case of American engines, had been brought over from the USA as deck cargo. To counter this problem the engines were inhibited at source under close inspection, after manufacture, after installation if the aircraft were to be stored, or if they were to be cased and stored. Because of the large numbers of engines in use and the always urgent time factor of WW2 operations, a compressed-air Oil Primer Mk 2 was brought into service for use when an engine was brought back into service after having been inhibited. The object was to force oil to the main bearings so that these were not starved of oil during the initial start-up period. Pressure air for the primer was supplied by either a foot or hand pump or a pneumatic servicing trolley, to two air vessels which gave the primer the capability to prime two or three engines with one gallon (4.54 litres) of fluid, delivered through a 16ft (4.8m) flexible hose at 60psi (4.2kg/sq. cm) pressure in about four minutes from a 4½-gallon (20.5-litre) container. The primer was mounted on a two-wheel, hand-pushed trolley supplied with air and oil gauges. Weight was 200lb (91kg).

The same problem of protecting engine interiors from corrosion applied to the gas turbine engines and an inhibiting rig was produced for the purpose, the Mk 3. This rig introduces oil under pressure to the inlet side of the high-pressure fuel pump, which causes the pump to act like a hydraulic motor, turning the engine over. At the same time the oil forces the fuel out of the system, replacing it with oil and thus inhibiting the entire engine system; and a protective spray is applied by the compressor to prevent corrosion of the compressor blades. The inhibiting fluid is contained in a 20-gallon (91-litre)

A rig turbine washing, used to clean aircraft engine compressors while installed in the aircraft. RAF Stafford, 1993.

tank, from which it feeds by gravity to a Plessey pump driven by a 5hp electric motor from a 400/440V a/c three-phase, 50 cycle/min mains supply. The pump capacity is 3½ gallons (16 litres) per minute at 1250psi (87.9kg/sq. cm) at 1420rpm. Two flexible hoses, one each of delivery and return, and smaller drain hoses are provided for connecting the rig to the engine to be inhibited. Mounted on the right-hand side of the rig is an instrument panel and on the left is a hose storage compartment with controls. The rig is mounted on a wheeled trolley with hand-operated starting handle. Weight dry is 890lb (404kg) and wet 1092lb (496kg).

After storage and/or use of inhibitants, or even prior to an engine's return to service, the compressors of gas turbine engines are cleaned by the use of

a turbine compressor washing rig, introduced in the 1960s. This unit is designed to inject a predetermined amount of detergent emulsion at 4psi (0.28kg/sq. cm) into the air intake while the engine is run at idling speed. The solution is introduced into the compressor via a flexible hose from the rig to a hinged spray ring assembled around the air intake. The detergent is contained in two 5-gallon (23-litre) containers, a fluid supply tank and an air-settling tank, both mounted on a two-wheeled tubular steel trolley. Fitted to the supply tank is a dipstick and filler cap, and the container is pressurised via an external mains supply, a hand-operated pump or a compressed-air trolley; a pressure gauge is fitted to the settling tank. The rig also includes a fluid filter, air filter, pressure-relief valve and two shut-off control cocks.

Another GSE in this field is the High Pressure Lubricator type 8639UR, designed specifically for pressure lubrication with grease or oil. The lubricator can be used either from a hangar supply or a mobile compressor and consists of an air motor attached to a pump that forms an assembly, with a lid that clamps on to a 28lb (12.7kg) capacity container. The pump is immersed in the lubricant. A spring-loaded follower is used with the grease to assist scavenging of the container. The air motor delivers 6psi (0.42kg/sq. cm) maximum air supply to give a lubrication pressure of 2800psi (196.9kg/sq.cm) through a 30ft (9.1m) length delivery hose to the lubricator, which is fitted with a control valve and to which can be fitted a standard grease connector.

An example of specialist GSE for comparatively minor servicing is the Oil Filling Rig type 11565, for priming and draining items of equipment. This uses silicon fluid or water glycol as a cooling medium. The rig comprises a tubular steel two-wheeled trolley on which is mounted a tank for silicon fluid, an electrically driven pump, a filter, drain/prime valve, priming and draining hoses and a detachable water tank. A ⅓hp motor for the hydraulic pump is operated either by a 220/225V three-phase 50cps supply or a 380/400V supply, the hydraulic pump output pressure controlled to 15psi (1.05kg/sq. cm) by a pressure-regulating valve. Weight is 134lb (61kg).

A medium on which the mechanics of the aeroplane as we know it depend, and an essential ingredient in order to fly, is oil. At first, of course, it was used purely as an engine lubricant and for the easing of mechanical moving parts, but its infinite possibili-

An early Hydraulic Test Set Mk 1 of WW2 vintage, still in use for component testing with pressure up to 6000psi (421kg/sq. cm). The top has been removed for servicing. RAF Cosford, May 1986.

ties for the hydraulic operation under compression of aircraft systems was soon confirmed by its use in the front gun interrupter gear devised by Constantinesco. This allowed a machine gun to be fired between the revolving blades of a tractor propeller by a cam on the propshaft sending an impulse along a pipeline of oil to the gun trigger. The hydraulic principle of oil was used only in this field on aircraft until the arrival of the oleo strut for the main undercarriage leg, in which oil under compression and controlled in its movement by internal orifices which varied in size according to the loading on the strut, in conjunction with compressed air or rubber blocks, gave the aeroplane the firm shock-absorbing unit it needed for the rough surface aerodromes in general use.

It was the retractable undercarriage which began the breakthrough of power-operated systems. At first operated by laborious hand pump, hydraulic power was given the fillip it needed by the development of the engine-driven hydraulic pump. By WW2 all retractable undercarriages on British operational aircraft, with the exception of the Avro Anson, were hydraulically operated – a very few were electrically operated – and its increasing use on other aircraft functions such as flap operation led to the need for more efficient servicing, particularly as, unlike pneumatics which had perhaps two main manufacturers, the number of hydraulic power systems were bewildering in a service which would have benefited from fewer names and more standardisation. Among these were Bristol, Handley Page, Vickers, de Havilland, Dowty and Messier, which called for deep knowledge, specialist courses and a wider spectrum of servicing equipment.

Early hydraulic systems were relatively simple and required little GSE other than that of topping up oil reservoirs, but some systems incorporated compressed air-operated hydraulic accumulators for emergency operation of the undercarriage down, as well as providing a cushion against the sudden

Low-pressure Pneumatic Servicing Trolley Mk 1B. A trolley used for general pneumatic requirements, tyre inflation, sand blasting, pneumatic tools, paint spraying, etc. It comprises a Petter petrol engine, compressor, air receiver, regulating and reducing valves mounted on a two-wheeled weather-protected trolley. The unit is towable, with stabilising legs fitted when in use. Air is supplied from 5–100psi (0.351–7.03kg/sq. cm).

Hydraulic Component Test Rig. Used for the testing of modern aircraft hydraulic components up to 5000psi (351kg/sq. cm), but with the aid of special pumps and an intensifier circuit this pressure can be increased to 6000psi (422kg/sq. cm) and 10000psi (70.3kg/sq. cm) respectively. The hydraulic system has three circuits and is powered by a 400/440V electric motor.

shock of selection. These accumulators usually required an external source of air supply for their charging, and this was supplied from a mobile compressor.

The rapid adoption of engine-driven pumps, controls, pressure relief and other valves, filters, operating jacks, indicator and warning lights built up a system which required constant surveillance to maintain it at peak efficiency. Carrying out the essential servicing often required the aeroplane to be jacked up, so jacking GSE was needed. As a result of ground functioning or a reported fault, it might be necessary to test individual components and for this purpose a static test rig was built locally on most stations. These rigs were first made in station workshops and were designed to test a range of components by the application of static pressure (pressure without flow). Items as used in the aircraft system were built into a replica test system on a suitable bench and operated by a hand pump – these included the reservoir, filters, valves and pressure gauge. To this system would be substituted the actual components to be tested from the aircraft.

The experience gained from using the rig was incorporated into an official GSE known as the Hydraulic Test Set and issued to units during the latter half of WW2. It comprised a sheet-metal bed mounted on angle-iron legs; on the bed were fitted components of the particular maker's hydraulic system for which the set was to be used. Two hand pumps were fitted on a fascia along with pressure gauges, control valves, a hand-operated rotary pump for applying pressure into the system and an intensifier for further increasing the test pressure above normal, as required. With this test set a variety of test pressures up to 6000psi (422kg/sq. cm) could be generated, and most hydraulic components could be tested by fitting adaptors to suit a wide range. This test set remained in service for many years, but as later jet aircraft were introduced with more sophisticated systems and higher operating pressures, so suitable test rigs were required and acquired.

The hydraulic component test rig was a much larger item with a more comprehensive layout and was built in the early 1960s by HML, who specialised in this GSE. The unit consisted of a totally enclosed framework structure in which were mounted the hydraulic components and a 25-gallon (114-litre) tank; it incorporated a workbench, a fascia instrument panel and a front control panel. It had three hydraulic circuits, a power-operated

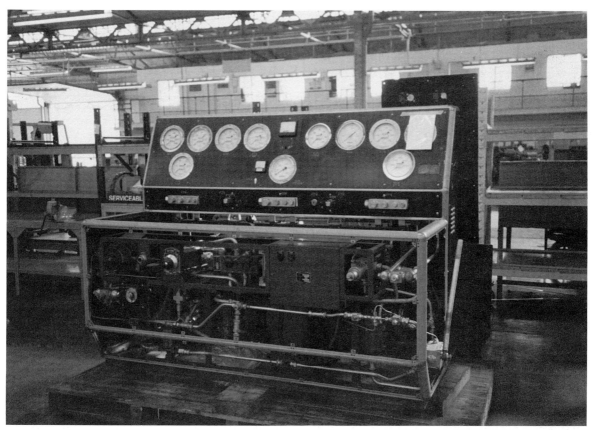

A Hydraulic Component Bench Test Set Mk 2 at RAF Stafford after servicing, 1993.

circuit which included two pumps driven by a 25hp electric motor of 400/440V ac 1500rpm, with a flow output controlled up to 5⅓-gallon (24-litre) per minute at pressures up to 5000psi (351kg/sq. cm); the hand pump set incorporated a Tangyes Hydra-Pak pump for use in pressure tests up to 6000psi (422kg/sq. cm) and for the intensifier set a Madan Junior air-hydro pump was operated from an external air, or nitrogen, pressure supply and was used to test components up to 10,000psi (703kg/sq. cm). Additionally, an electric motor was fitted and powered from a 230V a/c mains supply and incorporating a rectifier/transformer which converted a/c supply to 28V d/c for testing electrical/hydraulic components. An electric timing device could be set to control periods of 0–120 seconds, during which the a/c supply to a component under test could be switched on and off automatically.

The latest developments of these test benches are increasingly special-to-type and the introduction of the highly complex hydraulically powered flying controls required the use of one such special test rig. The Fairey Powered Flying Controls Test Rig Mk 2 was designed to test Fairey and Lockheed components. In addition it incorporated a filter flow unit for checking the 3-gallon (14-litre) per minute filters used in certain types of powered flying controls, by measuring the hydraulic pressure drop across the filter elements. In later use the special-to-type test benches tested equipment installed in such aircraft as the Harrier, Nimrod and Tornado. An example is the Hydraulic Test Set Mk 4, an Aerospace ground equipment (AGE) for the Tornado, which utilises a hangar-installed hydraulic ring main supply and can be used – as can the Mk 8 – for either hangar or dispersal work, according to the type of motor drive of the hydraulic pump.

Consistent with and complementary to the test rigs are the hydraulic servicing trolleys used for general servicing and maintenance of systems *in situ*. They became necessary because of continuous develop-

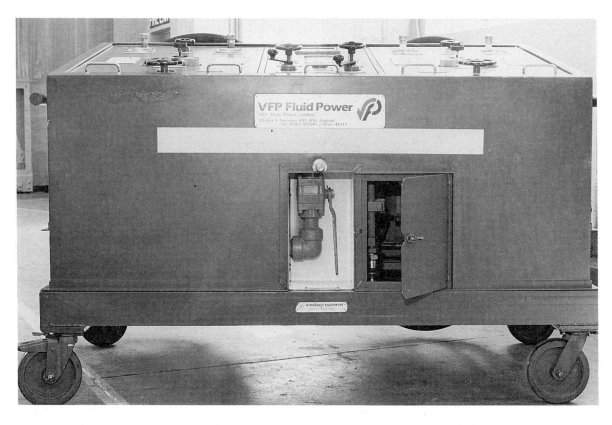

A Hydraulic Test Rig VFP Mk 4 used on the Tornado at RAF Cottesmore, June 1987.

ment by manufacturers to bring the systems to the present fine art. The result or benefit – and some penalty – of this is in the use of finer tolerances, higher operating pressures, better quality materials and oils. Servicing these systems requires a different type of unit which is among the first of the later prolific rash of units that came into service to set the trend for power operation, just as had the test rigs. This early unit was the small, two-wheeled Hydraulic Servicing Trolley Mks 2D, 2G and 3, which were similar in having a Coventry Victor engine, but of different type according to mark: 2D had a type AN4 Mk3 petrol; 2G a type HDA Mk2 twin-cylinder diesel; 3 a type AC4 Neptune petrol; all were suitable for testing systems up to 4000psi (281kg/sq. cm). The engine transmitted its drive to a gearbox by a lever-operated clutch; on the gearbox casing was provision for fitting a hydraulic pump of similar characteristics to that under test. Installed in the Mks 2D and 2G was a 5 micron filter, pressure-differential valve, pressure gauge and NRV to retain pressure in the system. The Mk 3 had a small hand pump, two HP filters and a pressure-differential relief valve. Engine speed could be varied to suit required pump speeds by reference to an indicator, and accessories for all the trolleys included a range of couplings to suit the various types of pumps and three 8ft (2.4m) hoses of varying bores and couplings. The Mk 2D trolleys had a third, self-castoring wheel and all trolleys were hand-pushed.

In the normal way of progress, as aircraft increased their range of hydraulic actuation, so a larger and more versatile trolley was required and the small two-wheeled Mk 2 series was superseded by larger four-wheeled towable trolleys, such as the Mk 5E, which could be used for high-pressure systems up to 4500psi (316kg/sq. cm). This trolley was powered by a Petter PJ4 four-cylinder diesel which drove a variable pump in the system. The trolley was protected by a steel canopy and panels against all weather, in which the RAF was now operating as a matter of course. Weight was 2248lb (1020kg). The Mk 10, designed and built by HML, was for hangar use, being powered by a very quiet

The Mk 4 test set (above) used in conjunction with a hydraulic ring main to activate the system of a Tornado under servicing at RAF Cottesmore, June 1987.

55W electric motor, which drove two axial-type pumps, each of 10-gallon (45-litre) output, either together or separately, on pump output pressures automatically set to give 280 bar. A 35-gallon (160-litre) capacity hydraulic oil tank was fitted with twin heat exchangers incorporating two electrically driven fans to maintain fluid at working temperatures. Full filtering and gauges ensured correct pressure and the loading and unloading of pumps was controlled by remote hand-held switches.

For use in dispersal areas where space was often at a premium, ML Aviation developed the very small Servicing Rig Mk 13A and for hangar use the Mk 13B. Both rigs are almost identical, differing only in that the 13A is powered by a Khol 181 single-cylinder engine and has detachable transport wheels as an option and the 13B is electrically powered by a Brook Compton Parkinson HWK 50hz 414V a/c motor. Both are mounted on a four-wheeled chassis and the units are designed to be operated by almost any untrained personnel, if necessary. Pump delivery can be regulated at between 300 and 2100psi (21.1–147.6kg/sq. cm) and has a flow controller which permits output from zero to 1.9 gallons (0 to 8.6 litres) per minute. The reservoir holds 2 gallons (9.1 litres) and weights are: Mk 13A 270lb (122kg), Mk 13B 138lb (63kg).

In aerial tactics, it had long been recognised that superiority at altitude was a prerequisite of fighter and reconnaissance aircraft. Fighter aircraft had been reaching the unprecedented height of 20,000ft (6096m) since mid-WW1 and went much higher after that, but the time spent usefully at these heights was conditioned by the oxygen supply, or lack of it. The new monoplane fighters and recce aircraft could easily operate at extreme heights with an adequate supply of oxygen. The open cockpits of the biplanes had begun to create a personal problem of comfort, which the enclosed cabins and cockpits of the new monoplanes had been designed to alleviate and pre-war pilots of such aircraft as the Bulldog, Fury and Gladiator had experimented with pressure suits for extreme altitude with some measure of success. But the suits were too restrictive to wear continually on standby, and it was decided to use them only as a temporary measure at first and to pressurise the cockpits of the new monoplane aircraft. Modified pressure suits came into their own well after WW2 for such aircraft as the Hunter, Lightning and later jet fighters. Most cabin aircraft relied on pressurisation of the full cabin. Early in WW2 the decision was made to pressurise high-altitude reconnaissance monoplanes.

Among the first high-altitude aircraft was the Spitfire Mk 6, which had been chosen for photo reconnaissance duties; pressurising gave the aircraft the advantage of several thousand feet more altitude before oxygen was needed; cabin pressure was set at 2psi (0.14kg/sq. cm), which also made the cockpit more comfortable. The pressure air was supplied from a Marshall cabin blower fitted to the engine(s) of pressurised aircraft. Other high-flying long-range aircraft soon followed suit.

The jet aircraft had solved one flight problem: it was ideal for the very high-altitude flying where its engine(s) performed at their best, which very much suited air-fighting tactics. The service and civilian passenger aircraft which were also able to operate at extreme heights gave crew and passengers the comfort of suitable pressurised cabins, with one difference. On the operational types the real possibility of battle damage resulting in lethal loss of pressurisation decreed that flying crews wear oxygen masks and, later, pressure suits. These latter were initially all right when flying at height but somewhat restricted on the ground and a form of cool ventilation had to be provided. So another piece of GSE was required to supply dehumidified air to ventilate the suits. Later type suits are more comfortable.

A Harrier in its hide being serviced with a Mk 8C hydraulic servicing trolley (in foreground), also showing the trestling arrangements with a fuselage spreader bar *(HML)*.

A hydraulic test rig Mk 8C designed for use on the Harrier/Jaguar aircraft after being serviced at RAF Stafford, July 1986.

A Mk 8C hydraulic test rig as above, showing the engine in the process of removal during deep servicing at RAF St Athan in May 1986.

Two views of a hydraulic servicing trolley Mk 11 after
completion of deep servicing at RAF Stafford, 1993.

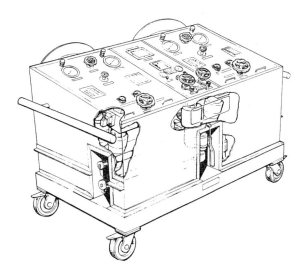

Hydraulic Test Console Mk 4. A combined in-line control and flow-dividing unit, designed for use in conjunction with a hydraulic mains supply for testing aircraft hydraulic systems. The console can provide two completely independent output circuits from a single supply, each with a flow rate of up to 40 gallons (180 litres) a minute.

The ventilation was supplied from the Air Supply Trolley Mk 1, introduced about 1955. This was a three-wheeled chassis on which was mounted a Sternes mechanical refrigeration plant powered by a Coventry Climax type ANA Mk 2 petrol engine to drive a Godfrey type J100 air blower. The blower drew in atmospheric air and forced it under pressure through the cooling plant and then through a water separator and distribution box. From the box six pressure suits could be serviced at once via their own flexible hoses. The trolley had a total output of 50 cu. ft (2.4cu. m) free air per minute at a pressure of 1psi (0.07kg/sq. cm) and the whole plant and controls were encased in sheet metal box structure and panels. Weight was 975lb (442kg).

The Mk 4 version of the above was redesigned as a larger unit, which used a Mk 3 version of the same engine to drive a Hall Mk 2 CP mechanical refriger-

A HML hydraulic servicing trolley is demonstrated on a BA Harrier. Some of the jacking arrangements for this aircraft can also be seen, together with the trolley connection points (HML).

ation plant and a Wade type 3R010 blower. For the cooling plant a 50ft (15m) delivery hose delivered the air to a connector communicating with the aircraft supply system or to a distributor head adaptor for the aircraft system supply pipes. Delivery was at 3lb (1.3kg) at 5psi (0.35kg/sq. cm) and was sufficient for three suits together. The chassis had a towing arm fitted with an adjustable jockey wheel and brakes; the mechanism and controls were covered with louvred sheet metal canopy and panels. Weight was 2100lb (952kg).

Testing the pressure cabins of high-altitude aircraft is an important servicing operation which requires checks on all areas of possible ingress and exit of air not essential to the system, plus checks of the cabin pressure itself, via the cabin pressure control valves. An external supply of air from such a test GSE as the Pressure Cabin Test Trolley

Hydraulic Servicing Trolley Mk 5E. A fully enclosed servicing trolley used for routine testing and servicing of hydraulic systems up to 4500psi (316kg/sq. cm) and powered by an air-cooled four-cylinder diesel engine driving a variable flow pump.

A Hydraulic Servicing Trolley Mk 3, after servicing at RAF Stafford in September 1986. This is an early type, used on the Avro Vulcan and still in use.

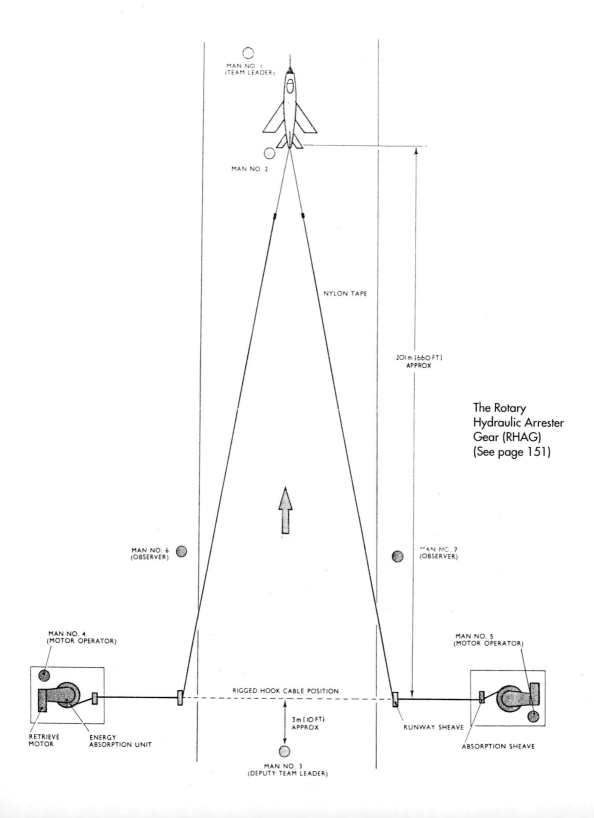

MAN NO. 1
(TEAM LEADER)

MAN NO. 2

NYLON TAPE

201m (660 FT)
APPROX

The Rotary
Hydraulic Arrester
Gear (RHAG)
(See page 151)

MAN NO. 6
(OBSERVER)

MAN NO. 7
(OBSERVER)

MAN NO. 4
(MOTOR OPERATOR)

MAN NO. 5
(MOTOR OPERATOR)

RIGGED HOOK CABLE POSITION

RUNWAY SHEAVE

3m (10 FT)
APPROX

RETRIEVE
MOTOR

ENERGY
ABSORPTION UNIT

ABSORPTION SHEAVE

MAN NO. 3
(DEPUTY TEAM LEADER)

Air Supply Trolley Mk 1. A specifically designed trolley to supply dehumidified air to the air-ventilated suits of aircrew waiting in aircraft on the ground prior to flight in warm weather. A Coventry petrol engine was used to drive an air blower. The trolley had a total output of 50 cu. ft of free air per minute at 10psi (1.41cu. m at 0.70kg/sq. cm).

Automatic Pilot Testing and Instrument Trolley 1B. A mobile unit for testing air pressure, suction-operated instruments and automatic pilots. Capable of supplying hot or cold filtered air up to 70psi (4.92kg/sq. cm) or a suction down to 5in (12.5cm) of mercury. The trolley is powered by a Petter engine.

Mk 1C, introduced in 1960, duplicates the normal engine supply. The trolley comprises a two-wheeled platform chassis carrying a Marshall type J100 compressor driven by a JAP model 35 engine and output of the trolley can be regulated to give between 30 and 110 cu.ft (0.85–3.1cu. m) of free air per minute at a pressure of 2 to 10psi (0.14–0.7kg/sq. cm), through a 2in (5cm) bore flexible hose used to connect the trolley to the aircraft under test. A hose adaptor is included for aircraft with smaller hose connections.

For testing air pressure and vacuum-operated instruments and auto pilots the Instrument and Auto Pilot Testing Trolley Mk 1B was a self-contained unit powered by a Petter PA1 engine, and was capable of supplying hot or cold filtered air at 70psi (4.92kg/sq. cm) or providing suction down to a partial vacuum of 5in (12.5cm) of mercury. Similar test rigs were available for pressure testing and vacuum testing pneumatically operated cabin pressure control and air-conditioning equipment, either *in situ* or out of the aircraft.

The post-war breed of aircraft began the era of sophisticated instrumentation and flight system circuitry, which included radio/radar, 'black box' electronics and navigational aids, to which were added as the years passed the wizardry of the Nimrod's identification systems and the Harrier, Phantom and Tornado attack electronics and electrics, making the air and ground electronic technician trades very vital indeed. It wasn't always so.

In the balmy days of flying in the 'best flying club in the world' the squadron electrician up to the early 1930s was overwhelmed with the task of checking the specific gravity of the 6/12V battery in each squadron aeroplane and ensuring that any bulbs had not fallen out. One electrician per flight was considered sufficient. And then it all happened. When the new monoplanes hit the squadrons the electricians were in business. The use of electrics increased dramatically in aircraft operation, electric motors being employed for flap actuation on some types, for jack operation, turret and bomb door operation, warning lights and alarms. There was also the electrical supply requirement for radio, soon to be followed by radar, and the increased instrumentation on every type and make of aircraft. The need for many more electricians to be trained for servicing these modern systems was obvious and the demand of day and night flying, both on and off the aircraft – night-flying electrical GSE was also greatly increased – meant that a whole new branch of electrical trades was required. And was supplied.

The electrical servicing required much new equipment and proper electrical workshops were laid down for the servicing of batteries, motors,

An Anthony Allen cabin pressurisation test rig, RAF Valley, September 1992.

dynamos and generators. Benches and test equipment was installed. Larger aircraft and more electrical operation began to impose a stress on the tradesmen's skills in terms of wartime demand and to alleviate this an Electrical Servicing Trolley Mk 1A was introduced. This trolley had a petrol engine which drove a suitable dynamo to generate the power supply for servicing an aircraft's electrical system. It had a control panel and was mobile, towable and weather-protected by canvas screens.

This first comparatively simple and rather basic GSE was the forerunner of increasingly complex units introduced to keep pace as aircraft became more and more dependent on electric actuation and the newer fields of microelectronics which were destined to supersede electrics to a large extent.

Among the first of this more comprehensive breed was Auto Diesel's Electrical Servicing Trolley, used to provide an electrical supply for servicing radio and radar equipment installed in aircraft with 200V three-phase 400cps installations. A six-wheeled chassis accommodated a power unit, a/c and d/c generators and associated equipment and controls,

An acoustically screened Cabin Pressure Test Trolley Mk 4, introduced in 1960 and shown here after servicing at RAF Cosford in September 1986.

and provided two sources of electrical supply which were available simultaneously, one of 200V a/c three phase 400cps at a continuous rating 60kVA and the other of 28V d/c at a continuous rating of 10kW. This trolley came in two versions, one with the generator powered by a Leyland 0680 diesel engine, the other with a 92hp slip ring induction motor which operated from a 415V three-phase 50cps mains supply. In both versions weather protection was by a fully enclosed steel canopy incorporating cable stowage. The units were towable.

This duality of power operation – the i/c engine for dispersal and remote use, the electric motor for hangar mains operation – was to be a feature of these trolleys for many years. The firm of Houchin produced a somewhat similar GSE for the ground servicing of aircraft requiring both a/c and d/c

current with output at 15kVA, also with two variants of power drive. One had a generator driven by a Ford series 209E six-cylinder petrol engine and the other had a 45hp electrical motor driven from a 415V three-phase 50cps mains supply. In both versions the equipment and controls were mounted on a four-wheeled chassis and enclosed by a sheet metal canopy, with provision for stowing cables and accessories in lockers.

The electrical servicing trolleys had acquired the more appropriate name of ground power units (GPU) and with the range of complex and more expensive equipment carried were becoming larger and heavier. As a result they required highly skilled ground-equipment tradesmen, or technicians, to service them. It is debatable whether the influx of these larger and heavier ground-servicing trolleys into an air force which prides itself on instant mobility assisted this mobility, but it certainly increased the work output of the aircraft system trades. One wonders if design should reverse its trend and produce aircraft which are more

A Murex ground power unit, one of the earliest types, used to start an English Electric Canberra's Sapphire engines at the 1953 SBA display *(Murex)*.

self-supporting in the servicing sector rather than relying so much on the plethora of external GSE.

Among the proliferating GPUs were those manufactured by Murex, one of the first, and ML, Auto Diesel and Houchin. An early Murex is described to give one an idea of the trend. To quote a blurb from this maker on the operating environment qualities of one of their latest units in about 1957 gives one an idea of their versatility even then: 'The unit can be operated in ambient temperatures of between -26°C and +44°C at sea level and stored in ambient temperatures of between -26°C and +70°C at a relative humidity of 95 per cent. The unit with canopy in normal closed position will be undamaged and will meet full performance specified herein when subjected to salt air, rain and snow driven by high winds up to 40mph from any direction.' Additionally, it was powered by a 105hp Cummins V504 diesel engine with four 12V batteries for engine

starting, each battery rated at 128amp/hr at a twenty-hour discharge rate, 34-gallon (155-litre) fuel tank, alternator control and protection. A control panel housed a most comprehensive list of instruments and controls for both the GPU and its engine. Provision was made for countering against five electrical faults occurring and one engine fault. As is the way of business, Murex increased their range of GPUs and were then superseded in the RAF by other makers.

In place of the old electrical generating sets the modern jet aircraft with their great reliance on electrical operation have the use of a Mobile Converter 30kVA, in conjunction with a DC generating set to provide alternating current for servicing the electrics/electronics. This GSE provides a maximum output of 30kVA at 200V a/c three-phase 400cps, for which it requires an input of 40kW d/c at 112V and 10kW d/c at 28V d/c input. The converter equipment includes a generator, control gear and instrumentation, input and output cables, all mounted on a four-wheeled chassis with sheet metal canopy. The equipment is cooled by air inlets in the canopy and,

An electrical starter trolley split to give access to the Cummins diesel engine power unit, which powers the generator. Station workshops, RAF Cottesmore, July 1987.

like the majority of these units, it is steerable, towable and fitted with brakes.

Another type of converter is the Frequency Converter type M400/15 used for hangar servicing, a small, compact, but rather heavy unit. The output supply of 200/115V three-phase 400Hz is for use in electrical servicing and as a power source for the aircraft. The converter comprises an electric motor with an input voltage of 380/415V three-phase 50Hz, a generator and exciter. A control box which can be mounted either on the motor casing or on a nearby wall contains all control and operating functions. Some stations have devised a local transporter frame to aid mobility. Weight of the unit is 838lb (380kg).

A most useful adjunct for hangar servicing to cope with the varying electrical-supply requirements is the Power Distribution Trolley Westair type 87 Mk 1, which provides a portable distribution ability to supply power for the operation of small power tools and lighting units. The incoming supply can be from any four pole protected sockets rated at 13amp or over and socket outlets on the trolley provide outgoing supplies as follows:

Three 230/250V 50Hz 5amp circuits
Five 110V 50Hz fluorescent lighting circuits for the type K handlamps
Four 24V 15amp circuits for the type Q flood-lights

The trolley can be used throughout the world subject to certain climatic limitations. It is quite light, weighing only 140lb (64kg).

It is probable that deep servicing might uncover suspect cracks, particularly on aircraft subject to high-speed manoeuvring, any of which could be

External view of a Trolley Electrical Servicing 25kVA at RAF Stafford, 1993.

vital to the safety of the aircraft. The great importance of detecting dangerous cracks had early been recognised, but despite metallurgical research and accurate heat treatments, they still occurred. The early method of testing was by the hot fluid chalk or cold fluid chalk tests, the former for small components which could be removed and the latter for fixed components. Both methods involved the use of paraffin, lubricating oil, French chalk and methylated spirits, the first heated to 194°F (90°C). Other methods included the magnetic flux test and it was on this item that the crack detector was based.

Aircraft metallurgy is based on the maximum strength for the lightest weight ratio and much of this is achieved by special heat treatment, but the great stresses to which some areas are subjected can create fatigue cracks and servicing inspections include checks for these. If cracks were suspected a hot or cold fluid chalk test was carried out. The method for the former was to heat a mixture of three

parts paraffin to one part lubricating oil to 194°F (90°C) in a bath and immerse the component for a period. The component was removed, cleaned and while still hot completely covered in French chalk; surplus chalk was removed and the component examined for a tell-tale yellowish stain which indicated the crack area. For the cold chalk test the suspect area was rubbed down with a similar mixture, cleaned and the area painted with a mixture of methylated spirit and French chalk. When the meths evaporated it left a thin residue of chalk in the area of the crack.

This older method was superseded by the magnaflux method which required the use of special equipment to magnetise steels and then observing the disturbance of the magnetic flux by the crack, or fault. This standard crack detector unit included accessories for current flow and magnetic flux application; crack-detecting ink was supplied from a self-contained reservoir in the unit and was conveyed by pump through a hose to the affected component. The detector was operated on an a/c supply of either 200/250V single-phase 40/60cps or 380/44V single-phase 40/60cps, and was installed in

A Trolley Electrical Servicing 60kVA powered by a mains electrical motor and modified locally by the General Engineering Flight of RAF Brize Norton to accept two flood-lights. June 1987.

workshops in a fixed position and enclosed with a steel sheet cover.

The foregoing methods may seem somewhat primitive and cumbersome against the latest electronic gadget, thermal imaging for crack detection. The equipment is highly sophisticated and expensive, but mobile and needing but one operator. It comprises a detector head unit mounted on a tripod; with read-out screens, the electronics pick up the difference of temperature between a newly landed aircraft's skin and any moisture trapped within a crack, and convert it to colour differences on the screens. This method allows a very rapid detection and surveillance of suspected cracks.

One ingenious GSE brought into service in the mid-1960s evolved as a result of leakage, or the possibility of leakage, occurring in refrigeration systems in aircraft. The purpose of the leak detector trolley was to apply a hot element leak detector to a refrigerant pack whilst it was still installed in an aircraft, which it achieved by using a detection nozzle on a 40ft (12m) hose from a remotely sited detector unit. The detection equipment comprised a control unit, detector head and blower unit contained in a control box mounted on a four-wheel, flat-base trolley. On the front of the trolley were two cable drums, one carrying the mains supply cable and the other the detector hose and earphone cable. The power supply required was 230V single-phase 50cps, maximum consumption being 250 watts. Sample air was delivered via the 40ft (12m) hose to the detector head which emitted audible signals to the earphones worn by the operator. If the refrigerant vapour was drawn in with the sample air, an increase in the rate of audible signals occurred and the presence of the refrigerant showed up visually on the meter.

When the first aero engines were removed from their flimsy airframes, after the propeller and

A Houchin 48kW generator at RAF Valley in September 1992.

A Countryman 7kW generator in use at RAF Valley, September 1992.

A JLO 415kVA mains 230V single-phase mobile generator for field use at RAF Cosford, July 1986.

disconnecting leads and pipes, etc., had been removed, they were probably lifted out by a couple of mechanics and most likely placed on the workbench or on an odd box. WW1 intensity of flying and servicing soon brought into use suitable engine stands which, although primitive, were suitable for both rotary/radial types and in-line engines. For the rotary/radial a wooden circular stand in which the engine was placed horizontally, for the in-line engine a four-legged trestle-like wood stand was used. These stands were developed into primitive test beds to take an engine for power checks, both being suitably strengthened; as engines increased in size and power so test beds grew in size to accommodate not only the engines but several of the mechanics involved in the testing. The early wooden stands gave way to all metal and the design became more specialised for the job. From the beginning every effort was made to evolve a general-purpose stand for the two groups of engines.

Engine stands were materially modified when some included dummy bulkheads and were used for one type of engine; the design incorporated similar engine-bearer pick-up points as the aircraft in which the engine was installed. They were suitably braced and fitted with castors for mobility. The last development of piston engine stands was the introduction of the power egg fitting when an engine complete with all its accessories was offered up as a complete plant to the aircraft. On removal the plant

A 12kW/115V three-phase 400Hz type M400/15 frequency converter in use on Tornado servicing at RAF Cottesmore in June 1987.

A Westair Power Distribution Trolley Mk 1 type 87 in use on BA Hawk servicing at RAF Valley in September 1992.

was placed complete in a special stand of a type which remained in use until the advent of the jet engine called for a different type and the stand cycle commenced again; this time without much success in standardisation due to the rapid development of the jet engine. These gas turbine stands were custom-built and eventually became quite massive for such engines as Olympus and Tay and RB211. A specialist stand for Tornado engine servicing is quite ingenious, with full electric power, a control box to operate the stand to an access angle and a nearby console for checking systems while in the stand.

A Petbow mobile load bank of 60kVA used for testing electrical servicing trolleys and also to simulate electrical loads of aircraft electrical generating equipment. RAF Stafford, July 1986.

A mobile engine test rig as used by 8 Squadron in 1918, with a Sunbeam Arab engine under test *(J.M. Bruce/S. Leslie Collection)*.

A fixed engine test rig at Marske in 1918, with a 130hp Clerget rotary engine under test. Quite a massive construction for the period *(Adkin Collection)*.

The major part of jet engine development was in producing ever higher thrust ratings, which led to problems, among them that of extreme danger in the areas of intake and exhaust flow during running. With 20,000lb (9070kg) plus of thrust let loose, care had to be exercised where the exhaust was pointing in addition to the extra decibels. So, inevitably, GSE was needed to alleviate this problem on servicing units and MUs, and a Universal Run-up Stand Mk 1 was introduced in the mid-1960s. This GSE was not intended for prolonged running and extensive testing and could be used only with engines under 4000lb (1815kg) in weight and a static thrust not exceeding 1500lb (680kg) and whose running adjustments required a fuel flow not exceeding 20 gallons (91 litres) per minute. But it was a step in the right direction.

The unit comprised the stand or trolley on which the engine was mounted, which was inserted into a universal stand and its controls connected up to a sound-resistant control cabin, which had double-glazed armour-plate windows and inter-communication with outside operators. The controls included start and stop speed regulators and performance assessment instruments. A fuel system was incorporated which comprised a

Trainee engine fitters at Reading carrying out a simulated bench test on a 120hp Beardmore engine type A–D, for the publicity camera. This part of the course was also used to teach propeller-swinging drill, as demonstrated by the air mechanic on the left.

A Rolls-Royce Merlin 22 shown on a stand designed for 'roll over' maintenance, allowing any part of the engine to be reached. Manchester Air and Space Museum, May 1983.

A Gnome rotary engine on a museum-made mobile engine test stand. Tanks for castor oil and petrol are at top right on the stand. RAF St Athan Museum, May 1986.

Mobile transportation stand for a Bristol Olympus at RAF St Athan in May 1986.

500-gallon (2273-litre) tank, electrically operated pumps, streamline filters, shut-off valves and connecting pipes. From this early model the RAF has eventually adopted manufacturer-type test beds, complete with mufflers.

There is, of course, a great variety of other stands in use, mostly to hold only one piece of equipment. Some of these can also transport equipment such as radar servicing trolleys, which are special stands used in the removal, transporting and installation of radar equipment. The type A is used for aircraft sets and consists of a four-wheeled chassis on which four stabilising legs are fitted. On the chassis is mounted a manually operated hoist which is hydraulically adjusted for height from 5ft 6in to 10ft (1.6–3m), a

platform for the tradesmen, toolbox and the rubber mountings for protecting the radar equipment on the platform. Maximum SWL of the hoist is 224lb (101kg). The type E is a stand on a sprung four-wheel trolley-type chassis, complete with the four radar assemblies mounted on the scanner frame, to enable the assemblies to be removed from the stand into bay servicing facilities. A unique feature is that the two rear wheels of the chassis can be retracted to

Turbo Union RB Tornado engines mounted for servicing on an electrically operated swivel jig, complete with control panel and access ladder, in the engine workshop at RAF Cottesmore in June 1987.

form a ramp to facilitate loading and offloading of the bench mounting. A bomb-loading hoist is stowed on the front of the trolley and mounted on the drawbar when not in use. Weight of the stand is 675lb (306kg).

A stand for use with the V bomber tail-warning radar heads was the type F. This unit had some of the features mentioned above, a towable four-wheel chassis on which was mounted a manually operated gantry with a maximum working load of 112lb (51kg), servicing operator's platform and a locker for storing two radar heads. The gantry was hydraulically adjusted for height between 9ft 4in

and 13ft (2.8–4m). Four stabilising legs were fitted and the weight was 860lb (390kg).

Helicopters are about the only aircraft which can treat tyre bursts with some small impunity, in an emergency. The modern tough tyres, allied to multi-wheel bogies, rarely fail, but because they are of such extreme importance, great care is taken with their checks. Before WW2 both tyre and inner tube and outer cover were repairable, vital in view of the quality of the tyres then and the greater damage from rough landing fields, and scrub if overseas. Where any doubt was felt of a tyre's condition, other than the obvious faults, it was removed – as it is now – for further examination to see if any damage was repairable within the repair scheme, which allowed inner tubes to be patch-repaired and, before and during WW2, outer covers to be repaired by the Dunlop Vulcanising process.

Close-up view of a Turbo Union RB 199 engine from a
Tornado in its servicing swivel jig, which appears to be an
adaptation of a test-bed jig. RAF Cottesmore, June 1987.

Engine stand for a Bristol Siddeley jet engine at RAF St
Athan in May 1986.

Leak Detector Trolley. A mobile unit for detecting refrigerant leaks in an aircraft refrigerant pack. The detection equipment comprises a control unit, detector head and blower unit within a control box mounted on a four-wheeled trolley. A 230V power supply is required. If refrigerant air is drawn in with sample air, an increased audible signal occurs and a warning is also indicated visually on a meter.

Radar Servicing Trolley Type E. Of different design to the type A, this trolley is bench-mounting on a reinforced sprung-wheel chassis. The bench-mounting supports the scanner, complete with four radar assemblies mounted on the scanner frame. The rear wheels of the chassis are retractable to facilitate loading on and off the bench-mounting with the aid of a type C bomb-loading hoist.

Radar Servicing Trolley Type A. For the servicing, removal, transportation and installation of aircraft radar units. A servicing personnel platform and manually operated crane with a toolbox is mounted on a four-wheeled trolley. The crane is adjusted vertically by hydraulic means and four stabilising legs are fitted.

This stand is half of a Radar Servicing Trolley type E with a scanner. The stand is normally transported on a four-wheeled, spring-loaded trolley which forms the other half. Manchester Air and Space Museum, October 1985.

Locally manufactured chassis with trolley accumulator wheels to transport a main wheel quickly in the event of a blown tyre on landing. Also part of a crash kit. RAF Cottesmore, June 1987.

A wheel-change dolly manufactured by Frank Brown and Sons and used to transport a TriStar main bogie wheel quickly in the event of a blown tyre on landing. RAF Cottesmore, June 1987.

Screw-type Tyre Separator. Designed to break the adhesion between the tyre bead and the inner side of the aircraft wheel flanges when removing tubeless tyres from wheels of up to 50in (127cm) in diameter, with a minimum bearing bore diameter of 1¼in (3.1cm).

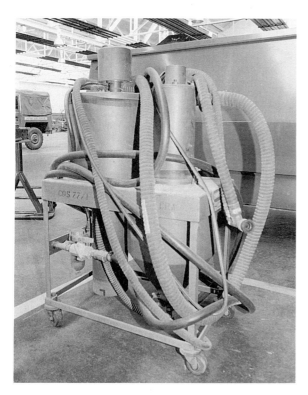

A vacuum blast-cleaning machine using an abrasive medium, for cleaning steel, aluminium, etc. RAF Cosford, September 1986.

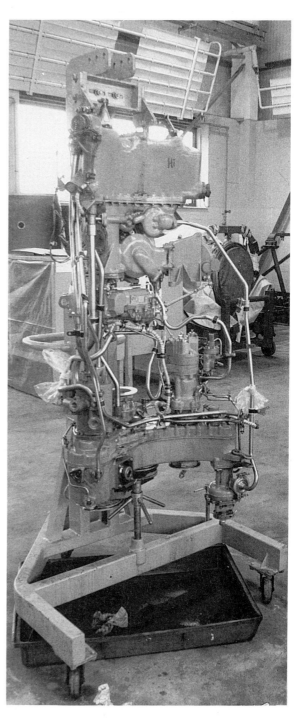

An 'accessory pack' stand used when dismantling and servicing Ardour engines of the BA Hawk, shown in the RAF Valley workshop in September 1992. The engine itself comprises three readily dismantled modules.

V V168 Hawk on maintenance. On the right of the picture a hydraulic test rig is in use. RAF Valley, September 1992.

In removing the cover the first GSE were tyre levers, and a good hefty wooden mallet to loosen the tyre bead from the wheel rim – after the tyre was deflated – and to remove the cover. If the tyre was to be vulcanised, the appropriate repair would be carried out on the complete wheel, using the Dunlop Vulcaniser. This was basically a heating element, to which was secured a number of sole plates which had the correct tyre curve to ensure that pressure could be applied to the centre of the repair, and to which a bar clamp was adjustably connected by a central screw. The vulcaniser was secured by a chain which ran from one end of the clamp, through the wheel hub and back to the other side of the clamp.

Pressure was applied on the patch by the adjusting screw and the vulcaniser switched on; main current on was shown by a red lamp.

The old method of loosening a tyre bead with tyre levers soon became inappropriate because of the risk of damaging the tyre bead and wheel rims, although the method was still practised by some units away from base, such as in the desert or scrub, where the niceties of modern GSE were not available. The tight fit caused by the serrated hubs and the better fitting tolerances which were needed when the inner tube was abandoned led to some difficulty in removing tyres; to assist the tradesmen a main wheel tyre separator was introduced. This handy GSE was a universal tool, consisting of a drawbar screwed at one end and fitted with a plate at the other. The drawbar was passed through the wheel hub and secured, a pressure ring of the required size was

A rigging jig used to check the correct setting of BA Hawk flap and ailerons. RAF Valley, September 1992.

passed over the bar with the ring against the tyre bead and a four-bar pressure boss was screwed down the screwbar to seat against the hub of the pressure ring. Suitable additional pressure pushed the tyre bead away from the wheel flange. Weight was a hefty 252lb (114kg) complete.

A further development of that GSE is the screw-type tyre separator, which is also used for breaking the adhesion when removing tubeless tyres from wheels up to 50in (127cm) in diameter and with a minimum bearing bore of 1¾in (4.4cm). The separator consists of a hinged steel frame adjustable to the centre height of the wheel assembly being dismantled, the frame raised or lowered by an

adjusting screw in the base. Fitted to each side frame is a circular plate on which is mounted one of a number of pressure rings to suit tyre and wheel size. One circular plate is fixed, the other moves transversely across the frame along a threaded drawbar manually operated by a ratchet spanner. The pressure rings have to contact the tyre sidewalls immediately outside the wheel flanges. Weight is 300lb (136kg).

Chasing a tyre and hub around the floor when fitting the tyre wasn't exactly good fitting practice, but that was the way it was until Dunlop designed the tyre fitting stand, which became a universal boon to all tyre bays, civilian included. The stand comprised a heavy steel circular base through the raised centre of which was secured a spindle on which a wheel clamp could be fitted at any number of positions. The wheel hub was placed over the

Transport trolley for Ardour engines of the BA Hawk, in use at RAF Valley, September 1992.

centre rod and clamped to the clamp plate. The tyre was placed in position with the lower bead fitted into the hub well; on the top of the centre spindle was placed the eye end of a roller, which was then adjusted to clear the wheel flange. The outer bead was then progressively rolled over the wheel flange into the hub.

INDEX